Motor Lawnmowers Owners Workshop Manual

by J.M.F. Parker

Models covered
Atco Commodore 14
Flymo TL Micromo
Hayter Hobby
Honda HR17
Honda HR194
Mountfield Emblem
Mountfield M3 Power Drive
Victa Silver Streak
Webb 14

(1085–5N1)

Haynes Publishing Group
Sparkford Nr Yeovil
Somerset BA22 7JJ England

Haynes Publications, Inc
861 Lawrence Drive
Newbury Park
California 91320 USA

ABCDE
FGHIJ
KLMNO
PQR

Acknowledgements

Pen Mill Motor Mowers Limited, Buckland Road, Pen Mill Trading Estate, Yeovil, Somerset, rendered valuable assistance, both material and advisory, in the writing of this book. Their directors Mr. Paul Horsey and Mr. Les Foy are cordially thanked for their help and support.

Garden and Lawn Equipment Ltd, of 85, Bristol Road, Whitchurch, Bristol were also extremely helpful with both marketing information and technical hints and tips. The owner Mr. Brian Shepherd is accorded appreciation for his patient attention. Our thanks are also due to Mr. N. Sergeant of W. Sergeant and Son, The Lawnmower Centre, 10 Broadway, Cheam, Surrey for general advice.

© Haynes Publishing Group 1985, 1988

A book in the **Haynes Owners Workshop Manual Series**

Printed by J.H. Haynes & Co. Ltd, Sparkford, Nr Yeovil, Somerset BA22 7JJ, England

ISBN 1 85010 085 3

British Library Cataloguing in Publication Data
Parker, J.M.F.
    Motor lawnmowers 2 owners workshop manual.—
    (Haynes owners workshop manuals ISSN 0305-4446)
    1. Power lawn mowers—Maintenance and repair
    I. Title
    681'.7631   SB433.2
    ISBN 1-85010-085-3

Contents

About this manual

It is strongly recommended that Chapter 2 be studied first. This covers all general servicing instructions essential to a successful overhaul. They have been given separately so as to keep the illustrated step-by-step instructions for individual machines as short and easy to follow as possible.

At the end of each individual Chapter are the facts and figures on machine settings and adjustments for the various makes and types of engine.

The title page lists the actual machines dealt with. If your exact machine is not listed, it is likely that one very similar to it is, and if the engine you have is of a different type, it may be described in this manual when fitted to a different mower. See also the companion volume to this manual which covers another range of mowers.

Using this manual

Lawnmower manufacturers continually make changes to specifications and recommendations, and these, when notified, are incorporated into our manuals at the earliest opportunity.

Whilst every care is taken to ensure that the information in this manual is correct no liability can be accepted by the author or publishers for loss, damage or injury caused by any errors in or omission from the information given.

Safety First!

Professional motor mechanics are trained in safe working procedures. However enthusiastic you may be about getting on with the job in hand, do take the time to ensure that your safety is not put at risk. A moment's lack of attention can result in an accident, as can failure to observe certain elementary precautions.

There will always be new ways of having accidents, and the following points do not pretend to be a comprehensive list of all dangers; they are intended rather to make you aware of the risks and to encourage a safety-conscious approach to all work you carry out on your vehicle.

Essential DOs and DON'Ts

DON'T attempt to drain oil until you are sure it has cooled sufficiently to avoid scalding you.

DON'T grasp any part of the engine, exhaust or silencer without first ascertaining that it is sufficiently cool to avoid burning you.

DON'T syphon toxic liquids such as fuel by mouth, or allow them to remain on your skin.

DON'T inhale clutch lining dust – it is injurious to health.

DON'T allow any spilt oil or grease to remain on the floor – wipe it up straight away, before someone slips on it.

DON'T use ill-fitting spanners or other tools which may slip and cause injury.

DON'T attempt to lift a heavy component which may be beyond your capability – get assistance.

DON'T rush to finish a job, or take unverified short cuts.

DO take care when attempting to slacken a stubborn nut or bolt. It is generally better to pull on a spanner, rather than push, so that if slippage occurs you fall away from the mower rather than on to it.

DO wear eye protection when using power tools such as drill, sander, bench grinder etc.

DO use a barrier cream on your hands prior to undertaking dirty jobs – it will protect your skin from infection as well as making the dirt easier to remove afterwards; but make sure your hands aren't left slippery.

DO keep loose clothing (cuffs, tie etc) and long hair well out of the way of moving mechanical parts.

DO keep your work area tidy – it is only too easy to fall over articles left lying around.

DO exercise caution when compressing springs for removal or installation. Ensure that the tension is applied and released in a controlled manner, using suitable tools which preclude the possibility of the spring escaping violently.

DO carry out work in a logical sequence and check that everything is correctly assembled and tightened afterwards.

IF, in spite of following these precautions, you are unfortunate enough to injure yourself, seek medical attention as soon as possible.

Fire

Remember at all times that petrol is highly flammable. Never smoke, or have any kind of naked flame around, when working on the vehicle. But the risk does not end there – a spark caused by an electrical short-circuit, by two metal surfaces contacting each other, or even by static electricity built up in your body under certain conditions, can ignite petrol vapour, which in a confined space is highly explosive.

It is recommended that a fire extinguisher of a type suitable for fuel and electrical fires is kept handy in the garage or workplace at all times. Never try to extinguish a fuel or electrical fire with water.

Fumes

Certain fumes are highly toxic and can quickly cause unconsciousness and even death if inhaled to any extent. Petrol vapour comes into this category, as do the vapours from certain solvents such as trichloroethylene. Any draining or pouring of such volatile fluids should be done in a well ventilated area.

When using cleaning fluids and solvents, read the instructions carefully. Never use materials from unmarked containers – they may give off poisonous vapours.

Never run the engine of a motor lawnmower in an enclosed space such as a garage. Exhaust fumes contain carbon monoxide which is extremely poisonous; if you need to run the engine, always do so in the open air or at least have the rear of the vehicle outside the workplace.

Mains electricity

When using an electric power tool, inspection light etc which works from the mains, always ensure that the appliance is correctly connected to its plug and that, where necessary, it is properly earthed (grounded). Do not use such appliances in damp conditions and, again, beware of creating a spark or applying excessive heat in the vicinity of fuel or fuel vapour.

Ignition HT voltage

A severe electric shock can result from touching certain parts of the ignition system, such as the HT leads, when the engine is running or being turned, particularly if components are damp or the insulation is defective. Where an electronic ignition system is fitted, the HT voltage is much higher and could prove fatal.

Ordering spare parts

As indicated above, the number of different mowers in different sizes is large, and the number of variation in parts even larger. The only safe procedure is to make a note of the mower type and serial number; and the engine type, horsepower (or capacity) and serial number. Take the damaged or worn part, plus the parts of the assembly to which it belongs (for example, a starter or a carburettor), to your local agent or service depot with the information on the mower and engine types.

The agent or depot knows the latest spares situation. In some cases the part may no longer be made in that form but they will be able to obtain the correct replacement to the latest design which is suitable as a replacement and will give the same performance.

This may seem to be a little laborious but will make your task and theirs much easier and is by far the quickest method in the long run.

Faultfinding

1   Starting procedures

1   Every time the mower is used, top up the petrol (if a 4-stroke) or petrol-oil mixture in the proportions recommended (if a 2-stroke).

2   Top up the sump (4-stroke). Remember that oil is not only essential for avoiding undue engine wear, it helps to cool a hard-working engine.

3   Oil or grease mower parts (cylinder mowers). This helps keep out grass cuttings, grass juice, and dirt, all of which cause wear.

4   If of the self-propelled type, ensure clutches are disengaged.

5   Set choke (unless automatic choke). Use carburettor tickler or priming button.

6   Set control to start position, or set throttle about 1/3 way open.

2   Faultfinding

NOTES: It is assumed that starting procedures were correct.

It is assumed the starter is turning the engine over smartly. If not, it should be removed and the starter fault rectified.

Mower will not start
Check that the shorting-out strip is not touching the top of the plug.

If the shorting out connection is at the carburettor, check this does not foul any part and provide a way to earth.

Check the spark plug, remove and inspect.

If wet, petrol is getting there.

Hold with screw portion against engine and spin with starter. If no spark, remove the lead and hold it about $\frac{1}{16}$ in (1.5-2mm) from a clean part of the top of the cylinder head, and spin again. If there is a spark, the plug is faulty and needs renewing.

If no spark, check the contacts in the contact breaker for a spark.

If no spark there, check the connections through ignition system, for loose wires or screw fittings.

If the mower still will not start, change the capacitor.

If the plug is dry and there is a spark, check petrol is in tank, check fuel filter is not blocked, and check petrol line right through.

If the plug is wet and there is a spark check air cleaner is not choked.

IMPORTANT: Never run the engine without the air cleaner, even for a few moments.

If the air cleaner is clear, check the choke setting.

Check the carburettor adjustments.

Mower starts, but gives low power
Governor sticky or movement blocked.

Fuel restricted.

Throttle or mixture controls incorrectly set.

Blocked exhaust ports (2-strokes).

Dirty air filter.

Mower parts clogged with grass etc.

Badly adjusted chains or belts, and/or clutch out of adjustment, causing drag; tight chains and belts consume power.

Poor crankcase seal (2-strokes).

Faulty reed valve, or dirty reed valve (2-strokes).

Runs unevenly
Incorrect mixture setting, probably too rich, see carburettor adjustment.

Dirt in fuel moving about.

Sticky carburettor controls.

Blocked exhaust system.

Loose hand controls or cables which move with movements of mower.

Reed valve choked (2-strokes).

Engine misses when driving mower
Dirty spark plug: clean and then reset gap. Renew, if in poor condition.

Pitted contact breaker points: file smooth or renew points, and reset gap.

Contact breaker moving point arm sticky: remove, clean pivot, lubricate pivot with one drop of machine oil.

Valve clearance incorrect, or weak valve springs (4-strokes).

Carburettor adjustment incorrect, probably rich mixture needed.

Reed valve choked (2-strokes).

Engine knocks
Carbon in combustion chamber.

Flywheel loose: remove starter and check key in keyway of shaft is correctly located. Check Belleville washer has domed side uppermost and retighten securing nut.

NOTE: *If after checks performance still seems poor, the engine may need overhauling. A quick check on compression is as follows:*

        2-strokes   *Turn the engine slowly, one complete revolution. Repeat several times. There should be a distinct resistance to turning, but much more resistance during one half-turn than during the other half-turn.*

        4-strokes   *Spin engine the opposite way to normal running. There should be a sharp rebound.*

Chapter 1 Which Mower to Buy

A wide range of powered lawnmowers exists for the domestic user, each with its own merits, and the fact that a particular mower is not included in this book should not exclude it from consideration by the potential buyer. Inclusion of all the machines available is not possible, and those covered are therefore limited to the more popular and readily available types, and those most typical of their kind. See also the companion volume to this work which covers a different range of mowers.

The saying that you get what you pay for is very true for motor lawnmowers. Those having the same or similar engine size, cutting width and broadly the same features are similar in price, provided that their quality is also more or less the same. Price variation largely depends on the complexity and number of features on offer. Therefore, carefully assess your particular requirements and the features that will meet them best, then buy the mower which provides these features. Avoid a lot of expensive features that you may never use; at worst you could end up with a mower so unsuited to your particular conditions that it is virtually unusable. For example, if you have steep inclines and a hilly lawn, consider a 2-stroke engine rather than a 4-stroke, because many 4-stroke engine lubrication systems will not work at high angles of inclination.

This chapter deals with the factors to be considered in simple terms and presents them in a way which should help the choice of the correct mower.

Classes of Mower

Broadly, there are two main classes of domestic powered lawnmowers: rotary mowers and cylinder mowers. The fundamental difference between the two is the cutting principle they use. Rotary mowers have a cutter rather like an aeroplane propeller laid flat so that it lies parallel with the ground that it passes over. It rotates at about 3,000 to 3,400 revolutions per minute, cutting the grass to the height at which it has been set. Most have a simple hand-operated adjustment that raises or lowers the whole mower to the required height of cut. Height can be adjusted in many mowers while the engine is running, but in view of the potential danger of high speed rotating cutters, **it is essential** to observe the manufacturer's instructions strictly when adjusting height of cut.

Cylinder Mowers

Cylinder mowers employ a number of blades, usually five, set round a central axle and curved slightly in a spiral. This assembly is cylindrical in shape and mounted horizontally in the mower. As the cutting cylinder rotates (at a much lower and quieter speed than rotary mower blades) the blades wipe past a stationary blade mounted under the mower. This gives a scissor effect between the stationary and rotating blades. The clearance between fixed and moving blades is ideally about the thickness of a cigarette paper, and has to be

maintained accurately at all times for efficient cutting. The precision in both manufacture and adjustment is one of the reasons why cylinder mowers are more expensive than rotaries. Another reason is the need for chain and clutch drives for the cutting cylinder and the travel drive to propel the mower. On the credit side, cylinder mowers give a much better finish to the lawn and provide a much more pronounced criss-cross pattern which is so satisfying to the eye.

The relative advantages and disadvantages of the two types are summarised later, but it should be borne in mind that neither type has a general superiority over the other.

Rotary Mowers

Three configurations of rotary mower are commonly available for the domestic user; the air cushion type which has no wheels but is supported by air from the engine-driven impeller, the wheeled self-propelled type, and finally the wheeled hand-propelled type which is pushed along and in which only the cutter blade is engine driven.

The air cushion type is the lightest of the three, thus allowing it to float on the air cushion without the need for a high powered engine, and also to enable it to be easily carried when the engine is not running. **Never** carry an air cushion rotary when the engine is running or you risk serious injury. 2-stroke engines are normally used on air cushion rotaries because they are lighter than equivalent 4-strokes. They give the added advantage of being capable of operation on nearly all inclines without lubrication problems.

Hand propelled rotary mowers are perfectly adequate for normal size gardens where the size of mower needed is not large enough to warrant a self-drive mower. Those fitted with a rear roller in place of rear wheels give a lawn finish approaching quite close to cylinder mower quality. To achieve good cutting, rotary mower blades have to turn very much faster than cylinder mower blades. This makes the rotary much noisier, and also means that the engine has to operate at near full throttle for most of its working life. Engine wear is thus higher than on a cylinder mower.

Rotary mowers will cut much longer grass than cylinder mowers, and can cope with much rougher and wetter conditions. However, their underside must be kept clean and free from impacted grass and soil, otherwise the aerodynamics which eject the grass cuttings are seriously impaired and clogging results.

Any vibration during operation of a rotary mower must be investigated and corrected immediately. An out of balance cutter will impart severe loads throughout the engine and do serious damage in a very short time.

Finally, **never** touch the cutter of a rotary engine unless the ignition cut-off switch has been set to off **and the plug lead disconnected.** Remember, a hot engine can fire if turned without the ignition being on. The kick or backfire from an engine is sufficient for the cutter to take fingers off or do other serious damage. Always wear strong footwear, and **never** plimsoles or sandals.

Rotary versus Cylinder Advantages/Disadvantages

Rotary	Cylinder
Relatively few moving parts hence cheaper for given width of cut.	Complicated drive arrangements hence greater expense.
Engine must operate near full throttle hence greater wear, more noise (especially blade noise) and greater fuel consumption	Engine can operate at any speed desired and mower still cuts. Smaller engine can cope with given width of cut.
Cutters are cheap to replace and easy to sharpen and maintain.	Cutter system more complicated, adjustment much more critical, maintenance of cutting edges needs professional attention. Properly adjusted they have a longer life than rotary cutters.
Will cut longer, wetter, rougher grass than cylinder mower.	Will cut to a better finish, but only cope with much shorter grass than rotary.
Perform better than cylinder mowers on inclines, subject to any lubrication limitations.	Not good on slopes due to roller skidding, higher risk of tipping over (higher c. of g.).
Cutting height easily adjusted.	Less easy on most types and requires use of tools. Some recent types (eg Atco Commodore) now have easy knob-type adjuster.
Stones and hard objects do less damage to cutters, which are more easily repaired.	Stones, etc trapped between cylinder and stationary blade easily ruin cutter system. Regrinding is professional job.
Out of balance cutter causes serious engine damage.	
Noisy.	Quiet. More all-round maintenance because of chains and drives.

Chapter 2 Overhauling and Servicing

Introduction

The hints and tips in this Chapter apply to some extent to all the mowers dealt with subsequently. To avoid continuous repetition in the individual Chapters they are gathered together here. They also provide the inexperienced overhauler with a largely common sense briefing on general aspects of overhauling and the attention that the various components are likely to need.

Preparation for Overhaul

Collect together all the spanners and other tools you are likely to need before starting work. It is no good discovering that a tool vital to further progress is missing when the mower is half stripped. Make sure that you know where all your other tools are, the ones you didn't think you'd need until something went wrong.

Have a supply of clean rags available. They should be lint free and not disintegrating, otherwise bits may collect in the engine and clog oilways.

A note pad and pencil should be readily to hand to note the positions of carburettor and governor link rods, springs etc. It is also wise to note which way round pistons are fitted, big endcaps fit on connecting rods and which holes valve followers were fitted in. Note this sort of information **before** the component is dismantled.

A number of boxes, containers or partitioned shelves should be available to put assemblies and components into after dismantling. This will prevent loss of parts and keep assemblies together as a reminder of which parts go where. It also keeps them clean.

Before attempting to dismantle the mower, thoroughly clean it down. When the engine has been removed and its cowlings taken off, clean it overall to remove every trace of congealed grease, grass particles etc. Examination cannot be effective with half the engine obscured.

Engine Externals

Check for broken cooling fins, signs of seepage from oil seals, missing nuts, bolts, clips, cracked castings and other damage. Look for oil leaks during the cleaning down process, but before the evidence is cleaned off. Broken fins reduce the cooling area and can cause hot running. Impeller blades which are broken or missing reduce the flow of cooling air and cause imbalance and hence vibration. Renew components with such damage.

Cylinder Head

After removal, clean the carbon from the combustion chamber with a wire brush. Do not damage the seating face. Inspect for cracks and if any are found penetrate deeply into the casting, renew the cylinder head. The most likely places for cracks to develop are from the sparking plug hole or from the bolt holes. Often they are extremely fine and very close inspection is needed to spot a hairline crack.

Cylinder

Look for scores in the cylinder bore. Most scores that occur are longitudinal and caused either by piston seizure or broken piston rings. They can only be corrected by a rebore out to a standard oversize, and the fitting of a new piston matched to the oversize bore. This requires professional equipment and skills.

Before removing a piston out through the top of a cylinder, take it to the bottom of the stroke, stuff the bore with rag and clean off the step of carbon at the top of the cylinder. If left, this step could jam a piston ring and break it as the piston is withdrawn. The rag will keep the particles from falling into the bore and when pulled out, should bring the bits of carbon with it. Check the bore dimension accurately for ovality. If greater than the manufacturer's limit, a rebore is necessary. This limit is normally about 0.003 inch.

Flywheel

Nearly all flywheels are held on a taper on the crankshaft. To separate them from the grip of the taper after removal of the flywheel nut, either use the correct puller as recommended by the engine manufacturer, or get an assistant to hold the weight of the engine by the flywheel, then using a soft hammer or soft metal block and ordinary hammer, strike the end of the crankshaft just hard enough to free the flywheel. Hold the engine just clear of the work top while doing this, or it may fall and be damaged. If the flywheel nut is refitted to strike with the hammer, the flywheel will not come right off and this will prevent dropping the engine. Whichever method is used, be very careful to use minimum force, or the threads on the crankshaft may be damaged or even snapped off. **Do not** use a legged extractor unless specifically instructed by the manufacturer, as these grip the edge of the flywheel and can easily crack the casting.

Piston

Piston rings should be removed with great care as they are brittle and easily broken. Insert strips of shim inside them and space them round the ring to spread it, then slide it off the piston. Carefully note which groove it came out of and which way up it was. If the same ring is to be reassembled later it must be located exactly as when removed. Clean out the groove to ensure that the rings will move freely in them. Sticking rings may break in the bore and cause scores.

Check the piston ring gaps to the manufacturer's dimension. To do this, clean the ends of the ring, insert into the bore about an inch down and level all the way round, then use a feeler gauge in the end gap.

Remove the gudgeon pin and check it for signs of wear, especially in the middle where the connecting rod little end fits. A good indication of little end and gudgeon pin wear can be obtained by rocking the connecting rod on the gudgeon pin. There should be virtually no side play.

Clean out the piston oil ways. Remove carbon from the top of the piston. **Do not deglaze the cylinder when fitting rings.**

Connecting Rod

Big end caps should always be replaced the same way round as they were originally. Most have ribs or markings on them to ensure correct assembly. Where these are absent, make suitable marks before dismantling or note existing marks in the note pad. Check the bearing surfaces and if worn, renew the rod and cap as a pair. At the same time, check the crank pin for wear or damage.

Connecting rods must be reassembled to the piston the correct way round, as noted during dismantling.

Crankcase

Before removing the cover from the crankcase, ensure that the key has been removed from the crankshaft. Clean up the surface of the crankshaft so that the bearing oil seal is not damaged as it is withdrawn with the cover.

Before reassembling components into the crankcase, thoroughly clean the interior to remove any solvents, cleaning material, lapping paste etc. Check both castings for cracks, stripped threads or other damage. Thread inserts of the right size can be used to repair stripped or damage threads. These work on the self-tapping principle and if effective are obviously very much cheaper than a new component.

Valves, Guides and Seats

Valve guide wear can only be rectified professionally by boring out and fitting bushes. These must then be reamed in correct relationship with the seats, using special equipment.

Valves can be ground in with lapping paste to re-establish good seating during overhaul, but too much grinding in will shroud the valves into the seats, and also may thin the valve head too much and cause "mushrooming". Whenever the valves are ground, the clearances will have to be reset by grinding off the tip of the valve stem. The tips must be ground square. Some mowers have adjuster caps on the stems which are ground in the same way as stems.

Bearings and Seals

Whenever a new bearing or oil seal is fitted, oil it first to ease the drive-in action. Seals have sharp lips on them; these should always face in towards the oil they are sealing. Drive the seals and the bearings in square with a drift or punch of the correct diameter.

Never drive ball bearings in by striking the inner race or the ball cage. Always place a tubular punch (or an old box spanner) of matching diameter on the outer race.

Carburettor

To check whether a float has a perforation, remove it from the carburettor and place it into very hot water. Bubbles will appear as the air in the float expands if there is a leak. Renew the float if this occurs.

Fit new washers and seals whenever a carburettor service is carried out. Seals from a carburettor which has been in use for an extended period will invariably have developed marks or "sets" which make them difficult to form an effective seal when refitted in a slightly different position.

Carefully note all spring and link positions before dismantling. Many carburettors have multiple production holes drilled in their controls to suit all applications. If connections to governors and throttle levers are not correct, the engine will not control properly. Nearly all modern mower engines rely on the governor system to maintain the engine speed in the operating range and to prevent damaging overspeeds. These are factory set and if lost, special equipment is necessary to re-establish them.

Silencer and Exhaust Ports

2-stroke engines in particular must have their silencer and exhaust ports thoroughly decarbonised. They are especially susceptible to carbon formation by the nature of their oil/petrol fuel mixture. Back pressure caused by reduction in the port or silencer gas flow area will have a marked effect on engine performance. Remove as much as possible by physical means. Immerse the components in caustic soda solution to remove the remainder, but take great care when using this solution as it is extremely harmful to skin and eyes. Use rubber gloves when handling the components or the solution, and preferably wear goggles. If the eyes should happen to be splashed, **immediately** rinse copiously with clean water and seek medical attention.

Reassembly

Oil the bearing surfaces of all shafts, followers, gears etc before assembling. This ensures that they do not run dry for the first few seconds after the initial start-up. It also protects seals as the shafts slide through them.

Torque loadings are not generally given as the average amateur is not likely to have a torque spanner and a set of matching sockets. If required, most agents will provide this information, but throughout this book, some indication of particularly important bolt tightening is indicated by the instruction "tighten firmly".

When using spanners, it is better to pull to tighten rather than push. Tightening tension can be gauged much more easily, and if the spanner slips it is much less likely that injury will follow. Also use a ring or box spanner wherever possible, in preference to a flat spanner. The latter slip more easily and are more prone to damage the flats.

Gaskets

Buy a new set before starting the job. It is false economy to re-use old gaskets. In particular, cylinder head gaskets must always be renewed.

Do not use jointing compounds unless specifically instructed.

Some engines rely on gasket thickness in conjunction with thrust washer thickness to set crankshaft end float. The combinations must be obtained from professional sources. Usually the need for this only arises if a new crankcase cover or crankshaft is fitted. It is normally sufficient to buy a gasket of the same thickness as the old one.

Recoil Starters

These are dealt with in the specific lawnmower chapters, as there are wide variations in their details. However, when renewing starter cords or fitting new handles to most starters that require a knot to secure them, the figure-of-eight knot shown below is the most effective method, and less likely to pull through. Heat seal the end of the cord to prevent fraying, by holding it momentarily in a naked flame.

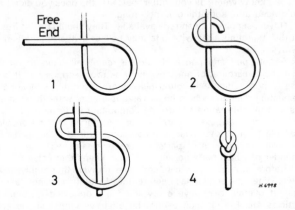

Rotary Cutters

Examine the cutting edges regularly. This will not only enable you to check their condition but also to look for nicks or more serious damage to the blades themselves. Small nicks can be filed away but with larger ones resharpening is not really practicable as so much of the metal has to be removed right along the blade edge: more seriously, balance will be affected and the other side must then be attended to both for safety and for the sake of avoiding engine damage through vibration.

Rotary cutters take many forms. Some cutter bars have an integral sharpened edge at each end, others have cutting blades bolted on. Cutting discs may have two blades, three blades, or two blades plus two grass deflectors. In all cases, these are bolted on. Some blades are triangular, giving three cutting edges which can be used in turn as they get blunted.

It is very important for safety to inspect all bolts and fittings very carefully. Any looseness must be investigated: is the locknut losing its grip? Is the shakefree washer (if fitted) too flattened or blunted to do its job? Is there any sign of the bolt hole becoming enlarged? If the enlargement is unmistakable then it is likely that the bolts will work loose again, despite the use of locknuts or other locking devices: a new disc is the only safe step here.

It goes without saying that the central fixing bolt holding the bar or disc to the end of the engine crankshaft must always be checked. Most of them are tightened down on a Belleville washer, with the domed surface **always** on the bolt head side. These washers are not merely washers, they are also springs, because of their shape, and the important advantage of this is that when parts settle down during the running of the mower, the Belleville washer still retains its pressure on the bolt and prevents it from loosening any further. Another advantage is that if the cutter strikes a heavy object it is free to give and spin round under the washer, which still retains its grip and continues to hold the cutter and make it turn again once the obstruction has been cleared.

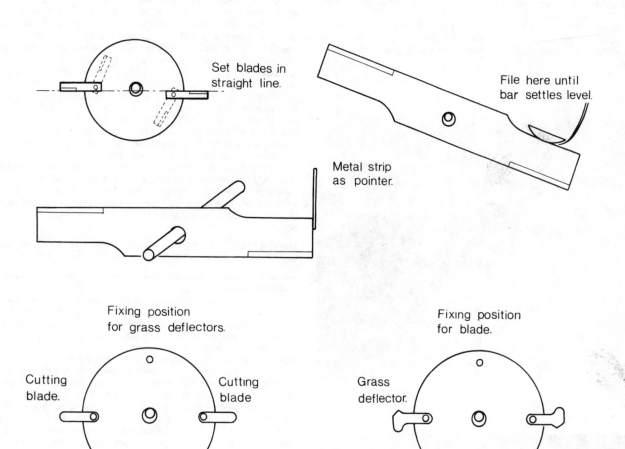

Set blades in straight line.

File here until bar settles level.

Metal strip as pointer.

Fixing position for grass deflectors.

Cutting blade.

Cutting blade

Fixing position for blade.

Grass deflector.

Balance check 1.

Balance check 2.

Balance check 3. With all fittings on. Check settling out point.

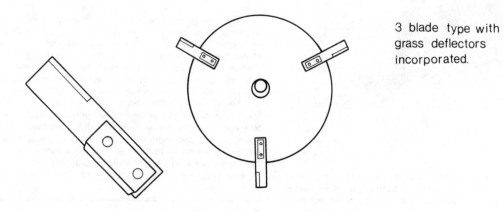

3 blade type with grass deflectors incorporated.

Sharpening

1   Sharpen to an angle of 30°, and keep the angle even all along the cutting edge, as shown here. Note that the back of the blade is turned up to form a grass deflector.

2   Do not sharpen to a point as this will quickly burr over and give a poor cutting edge. Leave a slight shoulder of about $\frac{1}{64}$ in (0.4 mm) as shown here. This will wear back slightly to give a good, long lasting edge.

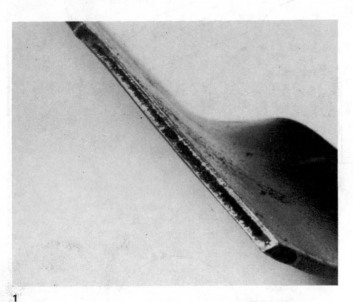

1

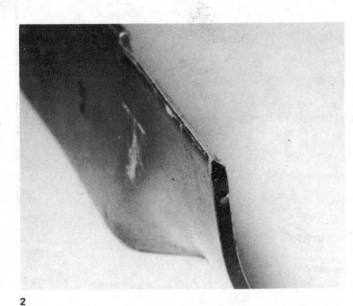

2

Balancing

Whatever the type of cutter, the general procedure is the same. One needs a thin steel rod, the smaller the better: this is supported firmly in a horizontal position and the bar or disc balanced on it through its fixing hole, as shown in the illustrations. For best results, the rod must be of much smaller diameter than the hole, and of course it must be straight.

3   Having been thoroughly cleaned, the bar or disc is supported on the rod. First, test the dimensions. Fix a thin strip of metal or other suitable pointer alongside the tip of one of the blades so that it just touches. Turn the bar or disc a half-circle until the other cutter is

against the pointer. The difference should not be more than $\frac{1}{16}$ in (1.5 mm).

4   Before correcting any difference, check the balance. Set the blades at the same height, with the bar parallel with the floor, and release gently. Unless the cutter bar or disc has been damaged, it is most likely that the longer side will dip towards the floor, showing it is out of balance. If so, make a few strokes of a file across the end of the longer part and recheck balance. Keep doing this until it no longer dips when released. As a check, turn it through a half-circle and check the balance again.

5   If the dimensions were correct, which is usually the case, but there is indication of being out of balance, file off the **back** of the bar or cutter, not the end. The secret with the filing is a little at a time. The better the all-round balance you can get, the more smoothly will the mower run and the less wear and strain there will be on the engine.

6   With a disc with four fittings, say two cutters and two grass deflectors, balance with the cutters only and then with the deflectors only. A disc with three blades is more difficult, but do a particularly careful check on their dimensions first. Then spin the disc several times to check whether it always tends to settle with one blade nearer the bottom. If so, it is likely that the disc assembly is slightly heavier at that point.

IMPORTANT: Bent blades, uneven length fittings or bars, and bent bars, are best discarded and new ones obtained and fitted.

Cylinder Cutters

No instructions have been given for regrinding the blades of cutting cylinders, because this is one operation which can only be carried out satisfactorily on a machine made specially for the purpose, such as those used in lawnmower repair establishments. It is worth considering the requirements for correct grinding.

The cutting cylinder may have anything from 3 blades, as on the smallest lightweight machines, to 7 blades on larger models in the higher price brackets. The blades may be straight or slightly curved; either way, they are set at an angle to the axle of the cylinder. All these blades do the cutting by a scissors action against the bottom blade. As each cylinder blade comes round and strokes the bottom blade, it is in contact with it at only one point at any given moment. Contact must therefore be maintained between the angled blade on the cylinder and the straight bottom blade all along its length, otherwise there will be gaps in the cutting.

Another way of looking at it is from either end, along the axle. Every part of every blade must describe a perfect circle of exactly the same diameter as it spins, so that all the blades together are rather like a cylinder (hence the name) whose outside edge is always in contact with the bottom blade. And this is only the start.

The surface of the cutting edge of the bottom blade is at an angle. Each blade on the cylinder must therefore be ground at the same angle. Multiply these requirements by from 3 to 7 times, and one would have to be a masochist to want to attempt doing the job at home!

The special grinding machines referred to can be adjusted to an accuracy of at least 0.4 mm ($\frac{1}{64}$ in). The cutting cylinder is supported in its own bearings, so that it spins as precisely as it does when in the mower. A grinding wheel, set at the required angle and driven by an electric motor, is mounted alongside on an accurant slide and passes from end to end of the cylinder, which is steadily spinning.

The cylinder has been sprayed with paint all over, so that as the grinding progresses it is easy to be sure when all the nicks and jags on the blades have been ground off, as only a straight smooth and paint-free edge can then be seen. When all blades have a complete cutting edge, smooth and clean and sharp, the machine is set to make several passes, grinding in both directions: this evens out any differences between the cutting edges and removes any slight roughness; it also dresses the grinding wheel itself in readiness for the next cylinder.

Bottom blade

It is possible to regrind a bottom blade which is in good condition although this is seldom worthwhile. To obtain the best performance from the refurbished cylinder it is best to renew the blade.

During use of a mower it may happen that a bottom blade, if rather lightweight and struck by some object, becomes bowed or dished. Obviously in this condition the scissors action cannot be complete at all points and poor cutting will result. It is sometimes possible to insert shims at its mounting points so that when screwed down it tends to straighten out.

Set the bottom blade so that it only just makes contact with the cylinder blades as the latter rotate. Too firm a contact wears both blade and cylinder cutting edges, causes noisy operation and puts an extra load on the engine.

To check cutting efficiency, hold a single thickness of thin paper across the bottom blade cutting edge, so that it points more or less at the cylinder axle, then carefully turn the cylinder by hand. **Be very careful as the blades are sharp enough to cause serious injury.** Scissor action between fixed and moving blades should cut the paper. Repeat at various points along the bottom blade, using all the cylinder blades. Ideally, the paper should be cut at any point along the bottom blade by any cylinder blade.

Some users may prefer to have a very slight clearance between the bottom blade and the cylinder blades; this gives very quiet operation while still giving a good cut, provided the blades are sharp.

Lapping

Grinding leaves slight roughness on one edge, which will be taken off against the bottom blade during mowing, the blade being further adjusted after 'running in'. If preferred, the cutting cylinder can be lapped.

Lapping compound can be obtained; it is usually oil mixed with grit, sizes between 100 and 300 microns, for this purpose. It is applied to the blades and the cylinder is turned backwards, in the opposite direction to mowing. Usually this can be done by fitting a brace on a nut on its shaft and turning by hand. Both the blades on the cylinder and the bottom blade and all fittings must be cleaned thoroughly afterwards as the grit will quickly damage moving parts such as bearings and chains. The bottom blade is set close for the operation, and after cleaning is readjusted and a paper cutting test carried out as described under the previous heading.

Lapping can also be used to sharpen up a slightly dulled set of blades. It can improve matters and give better mowing for a time, but cannot compensate for any nicks or chips in the blades; only grinding will remove these. Patent devices for 'grinding' at home, the 'work of a few minutes' and 'saving yourself mower repair depot charges' are really a variation of lapping and subject to the same limitations of being a temporary solution which has to be repeated after a comparatively short time. Only a grinding machine will give durable resharpening which will result in a high quality finish to a lawn.

Servicing

The aim of the following paragraphs is to suggest how to keep the mower in good working order, and to reduce deterioration caused by lack of routine attention or failure to rectify faults. The information covers servicing, running adjustments and minor repairs of the kind that arise during normal usage. Advice is given on how to assess the condition of a newly acquired second-hand mower and the maintenance it is likely to need before use. Some of the information is already contained elsewhere in the book in more detailed form, but is repeated here in simpler terms for convenience and quick reference.

General checks

These checks give a fairly accurate idea of the general condition of the mower and apply to both cylinder and rotary types. They are not a substitute for the more detailed examination necessary during stripping down, but if followed carefully they should indicate when there is a need to strip and examine more thoroughly.

1 Check the tightness and condition of all accessible nuts, bolts and screws. If nut and bolt flats are burred over or rounded off, or if the slots or crosses in screw heads are damaged, it indicates clumsy or inexpert attention. This could indicate a rough or slapdash approach to maintenance. Unless it is known for certain that the mower has been properly cared for, check that the routine maintenance in Chapter 2 has been done. If there is any doubt, carry out this maintenance before further use.

2 **Petrol tank.** Look through the filler hole into the tank for a build up of pieces of grass, particles of grit and soil or other sediment. If present, these may clog the filter inside the tank; the smaller particles may even get through the filter, causing damage to the fuel tap seats and blockage of the carburettor. To clean out, remove the tank and drain it. Let it dry out, then hold it upside down and shake the particles out through the filling hole. Swill round vigorously with a small quantity of petrol and empty to remove as much residue as possible. Repeat if necessary. **Do not attempt to rub or brush the mesh of the tank internal filter,** it is very fragile. In some mowers it forms a permanent part of the tank and cannot be replaced. To clean the tank filter, blow gently back through the tank outlet pipe. Check that the filler cap breather hole is clear: if blocked, fuel will not flow freely to the carburettor.

3 **Petrol pipes.** Check for kinking and splits, especially plastic pipes as these become hardened with age and crack easily. Splitting is most likely to occur at the ends where the pipe is pressed onto the tank and carburettor connections.

4 **Control cables.** Straighten out any kinks and replace broken sheaths. Tighten loose clips, straps and mountings, and replace any that are missing. Defects such as these impair control of the mower. Operate the control lever(s) while watching the other end of the cable and check that response of the appropriate mechanism is prompt. If not, readjust the cable to reduce lost motion. If there is undue resistance to lever movement, lubricate the cable and control pivots. **Do not lubricate friction devices**: these are designed to prevent control settings being altered by vibration, and will not work if oil gets into them.

5 **Electrical leads.** Check that they are not loose or in poor condition. Push spade connectors firmly onto their lugs and wriggle them slightly to ensure good contact. Clean off any oil contamination. Renew wires that have cracked insulation, broken strands or other damage. Make sure that clips, straps and securing devices are firmly attached and that none are broken or missing. Ensure that no lead runs too near a hot engine part (particularly the exhaust pipe) or a moving part. Check the high tension lead to the sparking plug especially; bend it, look for signs of cracks in the covering and renew if necessary. If hairline cracks in this covering are allowed to get near metal parts, shorting will occur (causing misfiring and poor starting). When shorting is suspected but cannot be pinned down, a good method of detection is to run the engine in total darkness with a torch ready to hand. Shorting will show up clearly as blue flashes. Mentally fix the flash position then switch the torch on to identify the trouble spot.

6 **Air filters and snorkels.** Remove and examine the filter element in the snorkel inlet housing. If coated in dust, or if the inside of the snorkel tube downstream of the element shows the slightest sign of dust, clean the parts thoroughly and fit a new element. Make sure that there are no cracks or holes in the trunking and renew it if necessary. The carburettor inlet filter usually consists of a polyurethane foam pad inside a housing. Remove the pad and check that it is clean. Some types need moistening with oil. If necessary, rinse the pad in petrol to clean it then wring out thoroughly. Pour about a tablespoon of clean engine oil onto the pad and wring it again to ensure complete dispersal throughout the foam, then replace it in the housing. If the foam has gone solid or lost its resilience, renew it, not forgetting to oil the new replacement.

7 **Engine oil.** Remove the dipstick gently to retain as much oil on it as possible. If the oil is black and thin looking, an oil change is essential. It is a wise precaution to change the oil in a second-hand mower regardless of appearance. If metal particles can be seen in the oil on the dipstick, assume bearing failure or equally serious trouble: strip the engine and investigate.

8 **Engine compression.** Poor compression is a strong indication that the engine needs overhauling. A quick method for checking compression is as follows:

2-strokes	Turn the engine slowly through one complete revolution. There should be a distinct resistance to turning, but much more resistance during one half-turn than during the other.
4-strokes	Spin the engine the opposite way from normal running. There should be a sharp rebound.

9 **Sparking plug.** Remove the plug and examine the colour of the central electrode and the ceramic around it. These should be pink or a pinkish buff if the carburettor mixture is set correctly. If a pale grey, the mixture is too weak and the engine will lack power and run hot; spitting back through the carburettor often accompanies this

condition. If the plug appears black and sooty, the mixture is too rich; the exhaust will probably be smoky and the tick-over uneven. In either case, adjust the mixture as required. Check the gap between the electrodes, it should be 0.025 – 0.028 in (0.7 – 0.75 mm) or as recommended by the engine manufacturer. If the electrodes are burnt away or the interior ceramic is cracked or chipped, fit a new plug of the recommended type. **Do not fit an incorrect grade of plug:** if, for example, a long reach plug is fitted to an engine designed for a short reach plug, an internal engine part may foul the plug causing serious engine damage.

10 **Points.** Check the gap between the contact breaker points if the engine is fitted with a conventional breaker ignition. The gap should be 0.020 in (0.51 mm) or as recommended by the engine manufacturer. Before checking the gap make sure the points are clean, i.e. there is not a pip on one point and a crater on the other. Small pips and craters can be cleaned off using a fine carborundum stone, but if large ones are present, fit new points. If new points quickly develop a new pip and crater, the condenser is weak and should be renewed. If the spark at the plug appears weak and yellowish rather than strong and blue, this could also mean a weak condenser. This is often confirmed by the engine starting when cold but misfiring and refusing to spark as it gets hotter. The fibre heel of the moving point should be lubricated with a small blob of grease where it bears on the cam sleeve.

11 **Valves** (4-stroke engine only). Check the clearance. If different from the engine manufacturer's recommendations, the clearance must be reset as described in the specialist lawnmower chapters. Note that the cylinder head must be removed before the valves can be removed to alter the clearance. To check the clearance, remove the cover from the valve chest (the cover usually incorporates the engine breather assembly) turn the engine to the top of the compression stroke, then slide a feeler gauge between the valve stem and the tappet. If the clearance is correct, further attention should not be necessary until the next seasonal overhaul.

12 **Crankcase breather valve** (4-stroke engines only). When fitted, this is usually situated in the valve chest. It can therefore be checked at the same time as the valve clearance. Check that the coil spring is not broken, and that the seating device seats properly and is not damaged or distorted.

13 **Reed valves** (2-stroke engines only). On engines fitted with reed valves, check that they are not bent, kinked or damaged. They should have gap under them of about 0.005 to 0.010 in (0.125 to 0.25 mm) or as recommended by the manufacturer. The reed valves are situated between the carburettor and the engine, usually in a mounting; it is therefore necessary to remove the carburettor and the mounting to inspect them.

Rotary mower checks

In addition to the general checks in the previous paragraphs, the following features found only in rotary mowers should also be checked.

1 **Cutters.** The cutter disc and its attachments, or the cutter bar, whichever is fitted, must be inspected frequently. Check that cutters and grass deflector bolts are tight, and that the cutters and deflectors lie in a straight line running through the centre of the disc. If they are bent or loose **they must be rectified immediately.** Do *not* run the engine with a missing, bent or loose deflector or cutter, as this will cause vibration which will seriously damage the engine (see Chapter 1). Loose parts on the cutter disc can fly off at high speed and cause serious injury. There must be no nicks or other damage to cutting edges and they should be sharp. A blunt cutter is not only inefficient, it causes the engine to labour because the grass drags the blade instead of being cut cleanly. Renew defective parts, **do not attempt to repair old parts.** Chapter 1 contains more detailed information on cutter defects. The method of sharpening and balancing the cutters is described earlier in this chapter.

2 **Cutter deck.** Check that the underside of the deck is clean. Dried grass and soil impacted onto this surface will alter the contours, spoil the aerodynamics and cause clogging and general inefficiency. Wash the surface with a scrubber and hosepipe immediately after use to prevent deposits hardening and building up. Worm casts especially cause this problem. Once hard, soil is extremely difficult to remove.

3 **Grass box.** Some boxes have louvres to assist the flow of air and grass into the box. Check that these louvres are not blocked. If the airflow is impeded, grass will clog in the airway under the mower.

4 **Height adjustment.** In some mowers, part of this mechanism is situated under the deck in a position exposed to soil and grass clogging. Function the adjustment over its whole range and check for full and free movement. Height adjustment tends to be left unused for long periods and can become rusted-up altogether. Lubricate and exercise it frequently. Where springs are fitted, keep them well greased as a protection against the corrosive juices from grass and greenstuff.

5 **Wheels.** Check wheel bearings for wear and lubrication, and check that the securing devices are sound and correctly fitted, i.e. no washers missing, split pins are of the correct size and not broken, spring clips properly seated, protective caps present and properly fitted. Most wheels are of plastic construction and do not have separate bearings. Renew wheels that are cracked or damaged, or that have badly worn bearing holes. Make sure that all wheels, and rollers on those mowers fitted with them, are lubricated.

6 **Handlebars.** Most handlebars are adjustable for height and should be checked for tightness. In non self-propelled mowers, ensure that the handlebars are not set too high, as this will cause the mower to dip at the front end when being pushed, lifting the rear end and causing uneven cutting.

Cylinder mower checks

1 As with rotary mowers, there are some features found only on cylinder mowers that need to be checked in addition to the general checks at the beginning of this section. Neglect makes itself felt much sooner in the cutting performance of a cylinder mower than a rotary, although the effects are not so catastrophic, e.g. simple neglect of cutters does not wreck a cylinder mower engine the way it does a rotary mower engine. However a rotary mower will manage to keep removing grass after a fashion as long as the cutter keeps turning, but this is not true of a cylinder mower. The following checks are therefore essential to achieve good cutting.

2 **Cylinder.** Check the bearings at each end of the cutting cylinder. No play is acceptable, although a little end float is allowable in bush-type bearings. Check that they are lubricated. Ball or roller type bearings are often sealed and only lubricated during overhaul unless an oil hole is provided. Check each blade individually to ensure that it is not bent, burred or nicked at any point along its length. If it is, then the bottom blade is almost certainly damaged at the same point. Straightening and regrinding is a professional job demanding use of a special grinding machine. Check for corrosion on all cutting edges and rub any rust off with an oiled rag: **do not** file or stone it off, as cutting action will be spoiled. **Handle cylinders carefully, they are sharp enough to inflict serious injury.**

3 **Bottom blade.** Check that the bottom blade is straight, free from nicks and not corroded. Slightly dulled cutting edges on the bottom blade and the cylinder blades can be improved by lapping the cylinder and bottom blade together as described previously in this Chapter.

4 **Front rollers.** Check that the carrier is not bent, distorted or unevenly adjusted (one end of the rollers higher than the other). To do this, sight the front rollers against the rear roller and check that they are parallel. This can be achieved by crouching at the front of the mower while an assistant tips the handlebars to the ground. The parallelness of the bottom blade can also be checked at the same time. A further useful method is to place the mower on hard standing that is known to be flat, then check that the front and back rollers lie flat without the mower rocking diagonally.

5 On some mowers it is possible inadvertently to set the front rollers too high, so that the bottom blade drags along the grass and damages the lawn surface. Check for this when examining the front rollers.

6 **Chains.** Remove the chain cover(s) and check the condition of the sprocket teeth and the chain(s). If the teeth are worn down, hooked or broken off, renew the sprockets and the chains. Don't put worn or very old chains on new sprockets; old chains are almost certainly stretched and will soon ruin the new sprockets. Similarly, don't fit new chains onto old sprockets as this causes both to wear rapidly. Check the tension of the chains; if necessary, adjust the tensioner to give each chain about $\frac{1}{2}$ in (13 mm) of free movement in the middle of its run. If too tight, the chains will stretch; if too slack, they will jump over the teeth and cause them to become hooked.

7 **Belts.** In mowers fitted with drive belts, check the belt condition, especially the inner edge which runs in the pulley grooves. If it is cracked or shows signs of fraying, fit a new belt. Examine the pulleys for cracks or bent rims as these increase the rate of belt wear. Cracks

show up more easily in the V of the pulley where the surface is smooth and shiny. If the pulley flanges are bent in towards each other, the belt tends to ride up the V at this point and down again as it passes, continually varying belt tension and increasing belt wear. Defective pulleys should be renewed before new belts are fitted. Check the idler pulley spring; if the coils appear stretched or unevenly spaced renew the spring, otherwise it will not apply the correct belt tension. A weak spring is likely to cause belt slip.

8   **Clutches.** Dog clutches are of the 'in-or-out' type and have no friction linings to wear. They require no attention between strip down overhauls, other than to check that the operating mechanism return spring (where fitted) is in good condition (not broken, coils evenly spaced and no apparent signs of weakness). Shoe type clutches are usually of the self-operating centrifugal type and are fitted with linings; check that the linings are not worn down to the rivets. If the rivet heads are found to be flush with the lining surface or, worse still, have bright marks showing that they have been rubbing on the metal of the clutch drum, **renew the linings before further use of the mower.** Check that the clutch parts are free of oil, do not lubricate them. Inspect the drum internally for scoring, especially if the rivet heads have been touching it.

9   Disc clutches contain several plates in a clutch housing. Friction plates, interposed between plain metal pressure plates, wear during service until eventually the clutch starts slipping. The plates can't be examined without dismantling the clutch, but if slipping occurs the friction plates must be renewed. Check for signs of oil contamination. If oil is allowed to spill onto the discs, clutch slip is likely and the friction plates may have to be renewed. It is sometimes possible to restore clutch operation by boiling all the plates in a strong detergent powder solution for five minutes, then boiling again in a fresh detergent solution. This should remove all traces of oil or grease from metal parts and friction material. If the metal plates are found to be blued or scored, they must be renewed. Blueing occurs if clutch slip is ignored and the plates become overheated by friction. It is much more likely to occur if the reason for slipping is oil on the plates.

Routine maintenance

1   **Lubrication**

(a)   Check the engine oil level before starting every time the mower is to be used (4-stroke engines only).

(b)   Change the oil every 25 hours of running, or more frequently under heavy duty or very dusty conditions (4-stroke engines only).

(c)   Periodically oil wheel bearings, roller axles, cylinder bearings (cylinder mowers only), height adjustment linkages and control cables and linkages.

(d)   Clean off the cutting edges of cylinder mowers after each mowing, using a well oiled rag.

2   **Carburettor.** The carburettor intake filter should be cleaned as described below under air cleaners and filters. Carburettor adjustment, once set, should not need regular attention. However, if it does become deranged, adjust the air mixture control as required. Occasionally clean the sediment out of the float chamber to prevent possible contamination of the float valve and jet(s). Dirt on the float valve will prevent it seating properly and cause flooding. Over a long period of time, petrol leaves a sticky deposit in the float chamber. For this reason, always turn the petrol off after mowing and let the engine run until it empties the float chamber. This prevents petrol from standing in the float chamber for cumulatively long periods.

3   **Air cleaners and filters.**

(a)   Remove dry element air cleaners every 3 hours of engine running, more often if conditions are dusty, and clean off dust by tapping them. Clean the inside of the housing before replacing the element.

(b)   Remove polyurethane foam filters every 3 hours of engine running and wash in solvent. Wring out thoroughly, dry and re-oil with about a teaspoonful of clean engine oil. Clean out the housing and replace the filter.

4   **Sparking plugs.**

(a)   Regularly remove the sparking plug, clean it and check that the gap is 0.70 to 0.75 mm (0.025 to 0.028 in). For convenience, do this at oil change intervals, or if misfiring or irregular running occurs. If the electrodes are burned away or the internal ceramic is cracked or chipped, renew the plug.

5   **Cutters.**

(a)   Cylinder mower cutting efficiency should be periodically checked as described earlier in this section under *Cylinder mower checks.*

(b)   Rotary mower cutter balance and condition should be checked frequently as described previously in this Chapter. An out of balance cutter can seriously damage the engine, and one with cutting edges in poor condition will cause the engine to labour. Clean and oil cutting edges.

6   **Cleaning.** The engine fins, flywheel screen and engine cowling apertures must be kept clean and free from obstruction to ensure a free flow of cooling air. Clean up any spilt oil immediately to prevent dust coagulation. Clean carburettor and governor linkages with a soft brush, **gently** to avoid damage or alteration of settings and spring tension. Clean off the juices from freshly cut greenery as these are corrosive. This applies especially to cutting edges.

7   **Grassboxes.** Clean out caked greenery, especially from rotary mower grassboxes which often have louvres to assist airflow. If these become blocked, the restricted airflow will not carry cuttings into the box properly and the mower will become clogged.

8   **Nuts, bolts and fixings.** Periodically go round all nuts, bolts and screws with the correct tool and check them for tightness. Fixings, clips and straps should all be checked for security and freedom from damage.

9   **Storage.** If the mower is not going to be used for 30 days or more, most mower manufacturers recommend carrying out the following storage procedure.

(a)   Drain the fuel from the tank into a container.

(b)   Drain the carburettor float chamber.

(c)   Drain the oil from 4-stroke engines when the engine is hot.

(d)   Replace the drain plug, fill the engine with 1 pint of paraffin and move the mower vigorously backwards and forwards to swill the paraffin round. Drain the paraffin out completely and refill with new engine oil to the full mark.

(e)   Thoroughly clean the engine, fins, flywheel screen, control cables and linkages.

(f)   Remove the sparking plug, pour 2 tablespoons of new oil in through the plug hole and turn the engine a few times to spread the oil. Replace the plug but leave the electrical lead off.

(g)   Turn the engine onto the compression stroke and leave it. This closes both valves to exclude moist air from the cylinder. It also ensures that if a valve sticks as a result of lengthy storage, the cam will open it next time the engine is turned and thus free it.

(h)   Cover the engine with a sack or cloth sheet. Do not use a polythene sheet as this collects condensation on the underside.

(i)   When the mower is next required for use, remove the sparking plug, clean it, check and set the gap, replace it, connect the lead and carry out a normal starting procedure. Use fresh petrol because stale petrol from the previous season may have deteriorated and could cause difficult starting. If starting is difficult remove the plug and preheat it using an oven grill or hotplate, or by playing a blow lamp flame on it. **Do not** heat it beyond its normal working temperature or damage may occur. Preheating disperses any condensation that may have formed and that could allow current to track to earth instead of sparking across the plug gap. Refit the plug, preferably while still hot, then start the engine promptly.

(j)   Before filling a 2-stroke petrol tank with petrol mixture, thoroughly rinse it with neat petrol to remove any oil film or sludge from the previous season.

(k)   The first engine start of the season is sometimes helped by removing the carburettor filter cover, **not the air cleaner element cap,** squirting a small quantity of petrol onto the element, replacing the cover and then starting the engine as normal. **Do not do this** if the first attempt to start flooded the engine. Check for flooding by removing and inspecting the plug; if it looks wet, the engine is flooded and both plug and engine must be left to dry out before another attempt to start.

Hayter Hobby

Chapter 3 Hayter Hobby

Introduction

The Hobby rotary lawn mower is hand-propelled on two wheels at the front and a split roller at the rear. It gives a 16 inch wide cut and the split roller enables a banded finish to be obtained. The example used for the dismantling and reassembly described in this Chapter was fitted with a Briggs and Stratton, 3hp, 4-stroke engine, but the Tecumseh LAV 153 4-stroke engine is also used for this mower. A single lever mounted in a quandrant on the handlebar controls engine operation, from Stop (engine cut-off), through slow and fast operation, to the choke position for starting from cold. Cutting height adjustment ranges from $\frac{1}{2}$ inch to 2 inches and is controlled by a single lever acting simultaneously on both wheels and the roller.

No automatic braking or drive disconnection is fitted in the cutter drive, and therefore the cutter rotates at high speed all the time the engine is running. It continues to rotate after engine switch-off until the engine becomes stationary. To avoid the risk of injury, **never put your hands or any implement underneath the casing when the engine is turning**. Similarly, never lift or tilt the mower to investigate grass blockages or for any other reason when the engine is still turning. Always stop the engine and pull the plug lead off before touching the cutter or clearing blockages.

A friction disc to which the cutter is attached, is designed to slip if the cutter hits a solid object, thus protecting the engine from shock loads and limiting cutter damage.

When the grassbox is removed, a deflector plate hinges down to stop particles and hard objects being ejected by the cutter and causing injury. **Do not raise the deflector while the engine is running** except to replace the grassbox. The mower can be used without the grassbox and with the deflector hinged down if grass collection is impaired by clogging in severe mowing conditions.

Dismantling

Read Chapter 2 for hints and tips on dismantling and reassembly before starting to dismantle. The information given there will assist an orderly and methodical approach to engine overhaul.

1 Disconnect the plug lead. Drain the oil from the engine.
2 Remove the cutter, friction disc and Woodruff key from the crankshaft.
3 Make a note of where the throttle cable is connected to the lever on the control plate i.e. in the hole of the lever nearest the cable clamp. Loosen the clamp, free the cable sheath and disconnect the cable from the lever.
4 Remove the engine from the main frame.
5 Remove the engine cowl complete with the recoil starter.
6 Remove the rotating screen from the flywheel.
7 Unscrew the recoil starter clutch housing anti-clockwise from the threads on the crankshaft (refer to reassembly later in the chapter for details on how this housing fits). Remove the housing and the keyed washer under it.
8 Disconnect the governor vane spring from the engine control plate lever, remove the control plate from the cylinder head then disconnect the ignition earth wire from underneath the control plate. Disconnection is achieved by pressing the spring clip and pulling the end of the wire out of the plastic holder.
9 Remove the governor vane bolt (which also secures one end of the ignition armature) to free the vane, unhook the governor link from the throttle butterfly and remove the vane.
10 Undo the remaining screw in the armature and remove the armature and coil.
11 Pull the breather pipe rubber elbow off the carburettor and remove the fuel tank complete with the carburettor.
12 Remove the cylinder head.
13 Remove the valves by prising up the collar, pulling it in the direction of the notch on the rim of the collar to free it from the valve stem then releasing it.
14 Remove the crankcase end plate.
15 Lift the oil slinger from the camshaft.
16 Withdraw the camshaft.
17 Remove the valve followers, marking them to ensure that on reassembly each is fitted in the hole from which it was removed.
18 Remove the big end cap from the connecting rod.
19 Remove the narrow ring of carbon from the top of the cylinder bore, using a soft tool to prevent damage to the bore, then withdraw the piston and connecting rod from the top of the cylinder. Be careful not to scratch the bore with the connecting rod during this operation.

Reassembly

1   To fit a new crankcase magneto bearing oil seal, prise out the old one with a screwdriver blade. Take care not to insert the blade too far or it may score the bore into which the seal fits. This could prevent proper seating of the new seal and lead to oil seepage. Smear the new seal with oil and tap it gently and evenly into place, with the sharp lip of the seal pointing towards the inside of the engine.

2   Check the condition of the crankshaft magneto bearing, camshaft bearing and cylinder bore for wear, scores or cracks. The bore is unsleeved aluminium and the bearings are unbushed aluminium. If the bore is damaged, worn oval or oversized (refer to the Technical Data at the end of this Chapter) professional skills and special equipment will be necessary to restore it. The same applies to worn or damaged bearings. These can be reamed out to accept bushes obtainable from the spares stockist, but special reaming equipment and a knowledge of how to use it are essential. Check all threaded holes for stripped threads and repair if necessary by fitting a thread insert of the correct size (refer to Chapter 2).

3   The valve components are shown in photo. Note the two conjoining holes in the centre of the collar that form an offset slot. This allows the larger hole to be fitted over the end of the valve stem. The collar is then moved sideways to seat the smaller hole under the shoulder of the valve stem, thus locking the valve and spring in the correct position. The shallow notch in the rim of the collar points in the direction in which the collar must be moved when removing the valve. Installing the valves is made easier if this notch is pointing outwards from the valve chest.

4   Fit the valve spring and collar into the valve chest, with the dished centre of the collar projecting upwards into the base of the spring. Insert the valve stem down through the valve guide and the coils of the spring. Using a screwdriver or the head of a spanner, prise the collar up against spring pressure and ease the valve stem through the larger hole. When the shoulder in the valve stem is through the collar, move the collar sideways until the smaller hole is fully seated under the shoulder, then release pressure.

5   Smear some oil onto the bearing journal at the taper end of the crankshaft and fit the crankshaft into the crankcase.

6   Fit the piston rings and assemble the gudgeon pin and connecting rod the same way round as noted when they were dismantled. Space the gaps in the piston rings 120° from each other. It is most important that the piston rings are fitted the same way up and in the same grooves of the piston as when originally fitted. Check the piston ring gaps as described in Chapter 2. The gap dimension is given in the Technical Data at the end of this chapter.

7   The connecting rod and big end cap are stepped at the two bolt holes in such a way that the cap will only seat onto the connecting rod when it is the correct way round (see the photo).

8   Smear the cylinder bore with oil. Using a piston ring clamp, fit the piston into the cylinder from the top by feeding the connecting rod through first. Ensure that the rod does not touch the cylinder walls and scratch them. Press the piston firmly into the cylinder, sliding it out of the piston clamp as the rings enter the bore. If necessary, use a piece of wood or a hammer handle and gently tap the piston out of the clamp and into the cylinder, but stop and investigate any undue resistance.

9   Smear some oil on the crankshaft journal and engage the big end onto the journal, with the bolt holes for the big end cap facing the cam gear side of the engine. Fit the big end cap and secure it with the two bolts and flat washers. Tighten the bolts very firmly as there are no locking devices, but do not overtighten. Rotate the crankshaft to ensure freedom of movement.

1

2

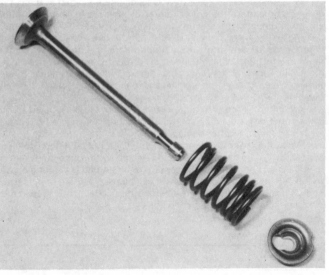

3

4

7

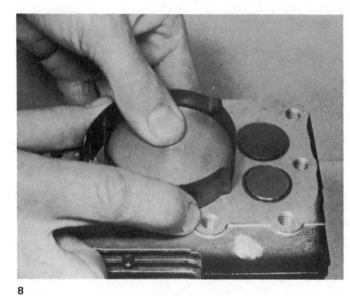

5

8

6

9

10 Put a drop of oil onto the cam followers and insert each follower into the same hole in the crankcase from which it was removed.

11 Turn the crankshaft until the timing mark on the gear is pointing at the middle of the camshaft bearing hole in the crankcase. Smear some oil on the camshaft bearing journal and install the camshaft. The timing dimple drilled in the camshaft gear must line up exactly with the mark on the crankshaft gear when the gears are meshed. Rotate the crankshaft a full turn in each direction to ensure correct movement.

12 Fit the oil slinger bracket onto the camshaft with the teeth of the plastic slinger in mesh with the cam gear. If the slinger teeth are worn or the fit of the slinger on the stub shaft is sloppy, renew the whole slinger assembly.

13 To fit a new crankcase cover main bearing oil seal, follow the same procedure as previously described for the crankcase magneto bearing oil seal.

12

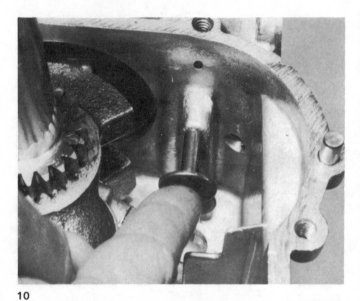

10

11

13

14 Check the condition of the crankcase cover main bearing and camshaft bearing for wear, scores and cracks. Damaged bearings can be reamed out and bushes fitted in the same manner as described previously for the crankcase, but professional skills and equipment are needed. Check all parts of the casting for cracks. If any are found, it is advisable to obtain a new casting. Attempts to repair cracks will not restore full working strength to the casting.

15 Apply a light coating of grease to the joint face of the crankcase cover and fit a new gasket. The grease will hold the gasket in positon and prevent it from puckering and being torn.

16 Smear some oil onto the crankshaft journal and the camshaft journal, then fit the crankcase cover, ensuring that the two double holes engage with the crankcase dowels correctly.

15

17

16

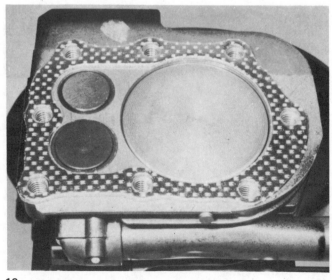

18

17 Fit the six cap bolts, working round them in diagonal sequence and tightening each a little at a time to avoid cracking the cover. Do not overtighten, as aluminium threads strip easily. Damaged or stripped threads should be fitted with a thread insert as described in Chapter 2. Check that the crankshaft endfloat is within the limits given in the Technical Data at the end of this Chapter. If less than the lower limit, an additional paper gasket must be used under the crankcase cover. If greater than the upper limit, a thrust washer is available and must be fitted on the crankshaft, between the cam drive gear and the crankcase cover. Additional paper gaskets may then be necessary to obtain acceptable endfloat. Never under any circumstances use gaskets of total thickness less than 0.015 inch (0.38 mm) thick.

18 With the piston at Top Dead Centre of the compression stroke, check the valve clearances which should be 0.005-0.007 in (0.13-0.18 mm) inlet and 0.009-0.011 in (0.23-0.28 mm) exhaust. This should always be done after crankcase assembly has been completed, thus ensuring that both ends of the camshaft are properly supported in the working position.

19 Fit a new cylinder head gasket. Do not use any jointing compound.

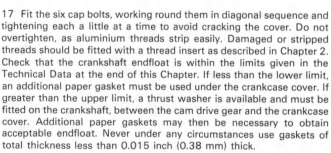
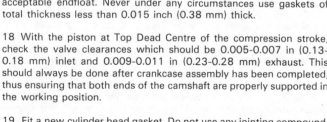

19

20 Fit the cylinder head, but do not tighten down the eight bolts at this stage, as three of them will have to be removed later to fit the linkage plate for the throttle lever and governor. Note: The three bolts nearest the exhaust port are longer than the others. **Do not fit them into the wrong holes** as they will bottom and, if tightening is continued, will strip the threads in the cylinder casting.

21 Check the fibre disc valve in the engine breather for distortion or cracks. A wire gauge 0.045 in (1.1 mm) thick should not enter the space between the disc valve and the body. A sparking plug wire gauge can be used for this check. The disc valve is held in place by an internal bracket which will be distorted if too much pressure is applied to the disc. Therefore, do not use force when checking with the wire gauge. If the disc valve is stuck or binding, or otherwise defective, renew the complete breather assembly.

22 Place a new gasket on the breather.

23 Fit the bolt at the left hand end of the breather first, then place the semi-circular profiled plate in position at the other end of the breather and fit the other bolt. Tighten the bolts evenly to ensure an oil tight seal by the gasket.

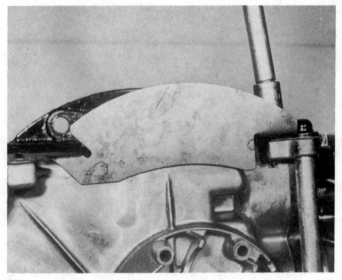

23

21

22

24 Ensure that the carburettor mounting face on the fuel tank is clean and undamaged. Check that the automatic choke calibrated hole in the side of the chamber is undamaged and free from obstruction. Do not us a pin to clear the hole or it may become burred or oversized, thus upsetting the accurate metering of air through it. If it cannot be cleared by blowing through it, use a nylon bristle as a soft probe.

25 Inspect the screen in the bottom of the fuel pipe for clealiness and freedom from damage and gum deposits. **Do not** brush or rub the screen to clean it, as it is very fragile and will almost certainly be damaged. Rinse the screen or blow it clean. If the screen is damaged, replace the nylon fuel pipe as the screen cannot be separated from it. The pipe is of snap-in type and may require considerable force to snap it into position. Check that the coils of the diaphragm spring alongside are not broken, kinked or otherwise damaged and that they are evenly spaced. Examine the diaphragm; if it is worn or torn, or has become stiff, fit a new one.

26 Examine the spirals of the choke return spring. They should not overlap on top of each other or be kinked or damaged. Gently turn the choke against the spring and ensure that it moves freely. It should return to its original position by spring pressure alone.

27 Fit the carburettor and diaphragm onto the fuel tank with the spring located in the hole in the bottom of the chamber.

28 With the cap removed from the choke operating link housing, gently move the link up and down and check for free movement and a positive spring return action.

29 Fit the cap to the choke link housing, taking care not to overtighten the screw and break the cap. Unscrew the needle valve beside the choke link housing and withdraw it, together with the spring and washer. Inspect the mixture needle; if it is grooved or bent, fit a new needle. Turn the needle **very gently** when screwing it in, until it just seats. The valve may be damaged if the needle is screwed in too far. After seating, unscrew the valve 1½ turns. This initial adjustment will permit the engine to be started later and warmed up for final adjustment. Check that the O-ring in the intake bore is not split or distorted, and that it is properly seated in the groove.

24

27

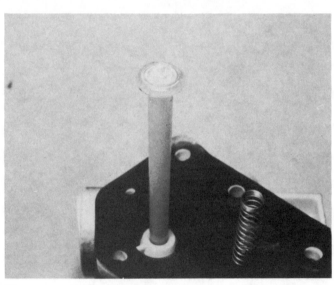

25

28

26

29

30 Press the rubber elbow onto the choke return spring housing.

31 Assemble the fuel tank to the engine. As the tank is offered into position, enter the inlet manifold into the carburettor intake, taking care not to damage or displace the intake O-ring. A smear of oil on the O-ring will help the manifold into the intake. At the same time as this connection is made, connect the emission pipe from the engine breather to the rubber elbow on the choke return spring housing. Secure the tank to the engine with a single bolt through the mounting lug near the filler cap. Use a spring washer under the bolt head.

32 Fit the ignition armature unit with the earthing lead passing behind the inlet manifold. Secure the coil temporarily by fitting the shorter of the two fixing bolts through the hole furthest from the carburettor.

33 Connect the armature earth lead .to the plastic holder on the underside of the engine control lever plate.

34 Fit the engine control plate on the cylinder head, then tighten the cylinder head down evenly and progressively on diagonally opposite bolts, so that the head is not distorted (torque is 140 lb/in).

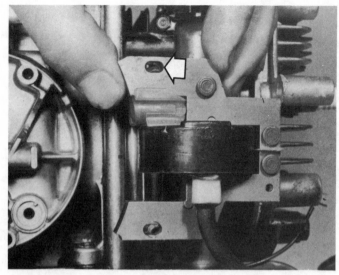

32

30

33

31

34

35 Connect the throttle butterfly link to the butterfly lever and to the end of the governor vane. Attach the coil spring to the end of the governor vane. Fit the governor vane by passing the special bolt through it and through the remaining hole in the armature. Do not fully tighten at this stage as the position of the armature will have to be adjusted after the flywheel has been fitted.

36 Attach the other end of the coil spring to the lever on the engine control plate.

37 Insert the flywheel key into the slot in the crankshaft (see arrow in photo). If the key has a shear mark on it or is otherwise damaged, its strength will be impaired. Discard it and fit a new one. **Do not use a steel key under any circumstances**. Use only a soft metal key of the type originally supplied.

38 Fit the flywheel, aligning the keyway with the crankshaft key. Tap the flywheel gently **on the central hub** to seat it on the taper. **Do not** hit it anywhere else but on the hub, or it may be cracked or the impeller fins broken off.

39 Fit the washer onto the crankshaft.

37

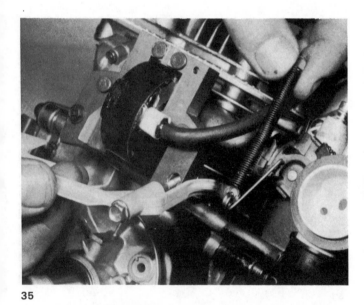

35

38

36

39

40 Screw the recoil starter clutch housing onto the threads on the crankshaft. Hold the other end of the crankshaft firmly in a soft jawed vice and tighten the clutch housing, using a spanner on the flats cast into the base of the housing. A cranked spanner will have to be used to avoid the impeller fins. If a cranked spanner is not available, an alternative method of tightening is to place the engine in a vice, with the flats on the housing held in the jaws but protected by two thin pieces of soft wood. The cutter friction disc can then be temporarily assembled to the drive end of the crankshaft and used to apply tightening torque.

41 Place the 6 steel balls in the starter clutch housing.

42 Position the clutch retainer cover on the clutch housing and tap it gently down over the shoulder on the housing.

43 Fit the deflector screen and secure with the two bolts.

44 Using a non-ferrous feeler gauge, set the air gap between the armature and the magnets in the rim of the flywheel to 0.010-0.014 in (0.25-0.36 mm). A piece of brass or aluminium of the right thickness will do if a proper feeler gauge is not available. Tighten the armature screws then check the air gap again. Do not use ordinary steel feeler gauges as they will weaken the magnets.

42

40

43

41

44

45

(9) Gently pull the handle until a good return tension can be felt, taking care not to allow the pulley to ride out of the housing, and hold the pulley at this tension.

(10) Pull the starter cord back into the housing until the handle is snugly against the side of the housing. Loop the surplus cord anti-clockwise round the pulley, then release the pulley tension, again taking care not to let the pulley ride out of the housing

(11) Secure the pulley in the housing by bending the two opposing metal tabs down to a minimum of $\frac{1}{16}$ inch from the face of the pulley. Note that two spare tabs are provided for use if a tab breaks while bending.

(12) Pull the handle a few times and check for free movement and correct recoil action.

46 Fit the cowl onto the engine, engaging the pulley hub onto the drive lobes of the ratchet (photo 46a). **Ensure that ...**

... the HT lead is positioned in the cut-out niche in the engine control linkage plate, otherwise it will be trapped by the cowl and possibly severed. Secure the cowl with the three bolts and flat washers (photo 46b).

47 Service the foam air filter as described in Chapter 2, then fit it into the housing with the four projections on the central cup **facing upwards**. If the cup is fitted upside down in the housing the filter will have no effect and engine wear will be considerably increased.

45 If the recoil starter cord fails to wind back into the rewind housing after being pulled, the most likely cause is a broken recoil spring. The spring is situated on top of the rope pulley, seen from underneath in the view above. To renew the spring proceed as follows:-

(1) Pull the knot out of the hollow starter handle, withdraw the plastic pin from the knot, undo the knot and remove the handle

(2) With the cowl resting upside down, bend up the two metal tabs that hold the pulley in the rewind housing and lift the pulley and rope clear.

(3) Note how one end of the broken spring hooks into the pulley hub and the other into the side of the rewind housing, then remove the broken parts

(4) Hook the inner end of the new spring into the hole in the inner hub of the pulley (no lubrication is needed for plastic pulleys). Ensure that the spring coils anti-clockwise out from the hub

(5) Support the loosely coiled spring against the pulley by hand, turn the pulley over and hold it immediately over the rewind housing. Hook the outer end of the spring into the slot in the side of the rewind housing

(6) Place the pulley and spring in the housing, turning the pulley anti-clockwise to tension the spring if the coils are spread too wide to fit into the housing. Do not bend the tabs down to secure the pulley in the housing at this stage

(7) Wind the starter cord anti-clockwise round the pulley, easing the latter up slightly from the housing if necessary, then thread the free end of the cord through the hole in the housing

(8) Thread the cord through the hole in the handle, then tie a figure of 8 knot around the plastic pin as shown below. Heat seal the end of the cord (see Chapter 2) then pull the knot and the pin into the hollow of the handle.

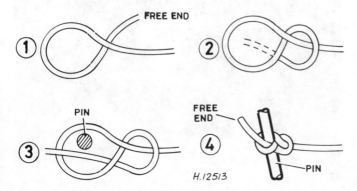

H.12513

46a

46b

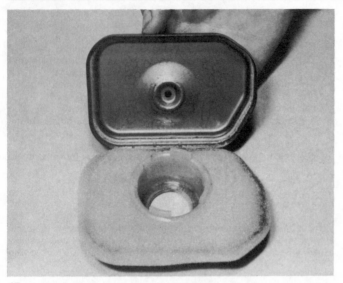

47

49

48 Fit the cover onto the filter housing, ensuring that the lip of the cover extends over the edge of the housing to form an effective seal. Secure the cover with the central screw.

49 Screw the exhaust silencer into the cylinder port.

50 Lift the engine onto the mainframe casting and secure it with the three bolts and flat washers. Note that the bolt on the left-hand side is also used to secure the underguard which encloses the height adjusting mechanism.

51 Fit the Woodruff key into the nearest of the two slots in the crankshaft.

52 Fit the friction disc assembly onto the crankshaft, with the groove in the hub correctly aligned with the Woodruff key on the crankshaft.

53 Attach the cutter bar to the crankshaft with cutter bar distance piece, spring washer and special bolt. Ensure that the cutter bar is the correct way round, with the deflectors pointing up into the mainframe.

54 Hold the end of the cutter bar, using a protective cloth to prevent injury from the cutting edge, and tighten the bolt firmly (torque setting is 40 ft/lb).

50

48

51

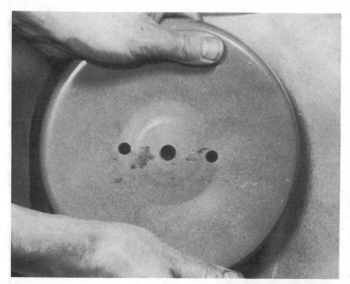

52

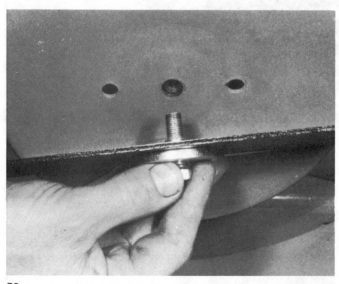

53

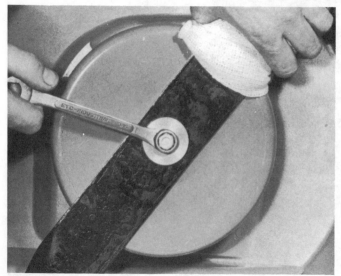

54

55 Connect the throttle cable into the nearer of the two holes in the lever, then secure the cable sheath under the clamp. Locate the sheath below the clamp screw to obtain the correct cable run. The sheath will probably be marked where it was previously clamped and should be clamped again in this position. To check that the position is correct, set the handlebar lever to the full throttle position and then check that the lever on the engine linkage plate is on the point of contact with the carburettor choke lever.

55

Technical data

Spark plug gap	0.030 in (0.75 mm)
Armature air gap	0.010 to 0.014 in (0.25 to 0.36 mm)
Valve clearance:	
Inlet	0.005 to 0.007 in (0.13 to 0.18 mm)
Exhaust	0.009 to 0.011 in (0.23 to 0.28 mm)
Breather disc valve clearance	0.045 in (1.1 mm) wire gauge must not enter space between valve and body
Crankshaft endfloat	0.002 to 0.008 in (0.05 mm to 0.20 mm)
Minimum crankcase cover gasket thickness	0.015 in (0.38 mm)
Ring gap not to exceed:	
compression rings	0.035 in (0.80 mm)
oil ring	0.045 in (1.14 mm)
Cylinder wear:	rebore if oversize greater than 0.003 in (0.08 mm) or ovality greater than 0.0025 in (0.06 mm)
Fuel type	90 to 94 octane

Oil	Summer (Above 40°F)	Winter Below 40°F
	SAE 30 or, if not available, use SAE 10W-30 or SAE 10W-40	SAE 5W-20 or SAE 5W-30 or, if not available, use SAE 10W or or SAE 10W-30

Mountfield Emblem

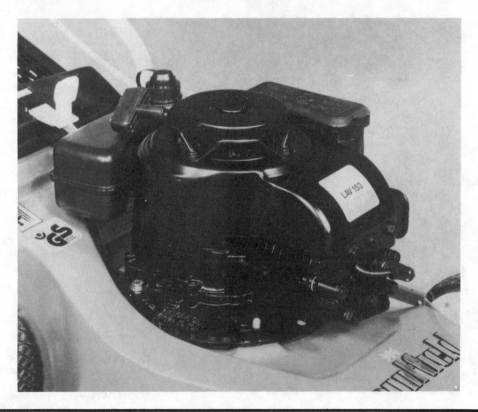

Chapter 4 Mountfield Emblem

Introduction

The Emblem is a hand-propelled rotary mower with a 15 inch wide cut. A Tecumseh LAV 153 4-stroke engine powered the cutter on the example used to compile this chapter. Engine control is by means of a single lever in a quadrant on the handle bar. Four positions are marked on the quadrant: Stop (engine cut-off), Slow, Fast and Choke (for starting from cold). Cutting height of the mower above the ground is set by a single lever acting on all four wheels simultaneously, to give an adjustment range of approximately 1.5 centimetres to 6 centimetres in eight, equally-spaced notches of lever movement.

No automatic brake or drive disconnection device is fitted to the cutter. Consequently it rotates at high speed all the time that the engine is running, and continues to rotate after engine switch-off until the engine becomes stationary. Therefore, **never put your hands or any implement underneath the casing when the engine is turning.** Serious injury can result if this fundamental safety rule is not observed. For the same reason, never lift the machine up to investigate grass cutting blockages or for any other reason when the engine is still turning. Always set the control lever to "Stop", wait for the engine to cease turning, then remove the lead from the plug before touching the cutter or clearing blocked passages.

A spring-loaded grass deflector plate drops down when the grass box is removed. The lever which is used to raise the deflector plate also forms a catch that holds the grassbox in place. The deflector stops particles and hard objects being ejected by the cutter and causing injury. Therefore, **do not raise the deflector while the engine is turning** except to replace the grassbox. If mowing conditions are so severe that grass collection by the box is impaired because of clogging, the grassbox can be removed and the mower worked with the deflector plate only. Before removing the grassbox, try raising the cutting height to improve the airflow and hence the grass collection capability.

Dismantling

Before starting to dismantle, read the general hints and tips in Chapter 2. These apply to all engines and if adopted, will ensure an orderly and methodical approach that will make both dismantling and reassembly much easier.

1 Disconnect the plug lead. Drain the oil from the engine.
2 Loosen the throttle cable clip at the carburettor, free the cable sheath and unhook the cable from the engine control plate lever. Make a note of the hole in the lever to which the cable was attached.

3 Remove the cutter from the end of the crankshaft, using a ring spanner on the bolt. Withdraw the spacer from the crankshaft, taking care not to lose the Woodruff key in the crankshaft slot.
4 Remove the two engine attachment screws and the nut and bolt near the oil filler hole, and lift the engine off the deck.
5 Pull the petrol pipe off the fuel tank connector fitting and lift the tank from the slide-off attachment slots on the engine cowl.
6 Remove the engine cowl.
7 Pull the snap-on lid off the air cleaner housing and remove the foam element.
8 Note the position of the holes in which the throttle butterfly link and the governor spring link fit. Remove the carburettor inlet manifold screws, lift the manifold and carburettor free, disconnect the links then remove the carburettor and manifold.
9 Remove the exhaust silencer.
10 Remove the flywheel and rotating screen (see Chapter 2 for advice on removing flywheels). Remove the crankshaft key.
11 Check that the ignition armature and coil unit is index marked for spark timing purposes (if not, mark it as shown in Reassembly later in this Chapter) then remove the unit.
12 Remove the cam sleeve from the crankshaft.
13 Remove the cylinder head and gasket.
14 Remove the breather assembly from the valve chest.
15 Remove the crankcase end cover. Remove the thrust shim from the crankshaft. Remove the oil pump body and plunger from the camshaft.
16 **Clearly mark** one side of the big end cap and the big end of the connecting rod to ensure that the cap is reassembled the correct way round, then remove the cap. Marking is essential as the cap will fit either way.
17 Remove the valves.
18 Remove the camshaft.
19 Remove the cam followers.
20 Remove the step of carbon at the top of the cylinder with a soft tool. This allows the piston to slide out easily during removal without damaging the piston rings.
21 Slide the piston and connecting rod out through the top of the cylinder, taking great care not to allow the connecting rod to scratch the cylinder bore.
22 Remove the crankshaft.
23 If the governor appears worn, remove it for inspection as follows:-

(1) Remove the top C-clip.
(2) Lift the spool off the governor shaft.
(3) Remove the bottom C-clip.
(4) Lift the governor plastic gear assembly and the spacer ring underneath it from the shaft

Reassembly

1   To fit a new crankcase magneto bearing oil seal, prise out the old seal with a screwdriver blade. Take care not to damage the bore into which the seal fits, as this could prevent the new seal from seating properly and may cause oil seepage. Smear the new seal with oil and tap it evenly into place, with the sharp lip of the seal pointing towards the inside of the engine.

2   Check the condition of the magneto bearing, the camshaft bearing and the cylinder bore for wear, scores or cracks. Like the Briggs and Stratton engine described in Chapter 3 for the Hayter Hobby, the cylinder bore is unsleeved aluminium and the bearings are unbushed aluminium. If the bore is worn oval or oversized (refer to the Technical Data at the end of this Chapter) then professional skills and special equipment will be necessary to repair it. The same applies to worn or damaged bearings. These can be reamed out to accept bushes obtainable from the spares stockist, but special reaming equipment and a knowledge of how to use it are essential. Check all threaded holes for stripped threads and repair if necessary by fitting a thread insert of the correct size (refer to Chapter 2).

3   The valve components are shown in photo. The spring retainer, which can be identified by the large symmetrical hole, must be fitted with its dished centre projecting into the middle of the spring coils. The collar, identified by the offset conjoining holes, locks the valve in position against coil spring pressure in exactly the same way as described in Chapter 3 for the Hayter Hobby engine.

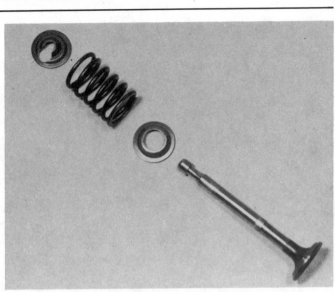
3

4   Fit the valve into the guide. Note that the exhaust valve being fitted above has a much smaller head than the inlet valve shown already fitted. The difference in size is so obvious that inadvertent assembly onto the wrong seat is virtually impossible. The valve seats are not removable and if badly burnt or pitted beyond recovery by normal valve grinding, they will have to be professionally recut. Valve guides can be renewed if worn, but will need reaming using special tools as described in Chapter 3.

5   Place the spring retainer over the valve stem and onto the end of the valve guide projecting into the valve chest. Fit the spring over the valve stem and seat it onto the retainer. Position the collar under the spring. Prise the collar up with a screwdriver so that the offset hole passes onto the valve system, then when level with the shoulder on the valve stem, move the collar sideways so that its smaller hole engages under the shoulder.

6   Smear oil on the crankcase magneto bearing and fit the crankshaft into the crankcase.

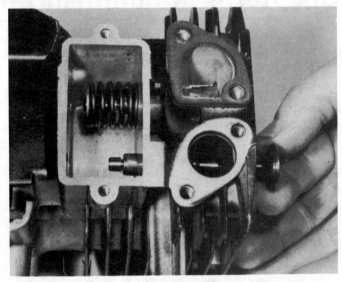
4

1

5

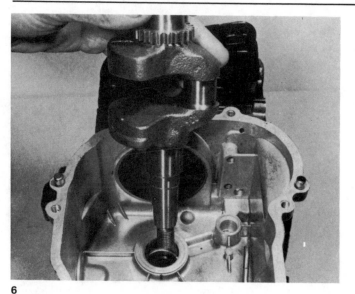

6

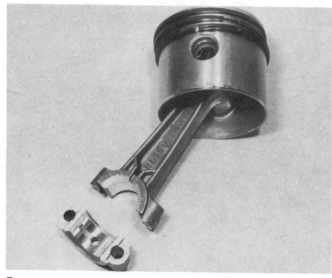

7

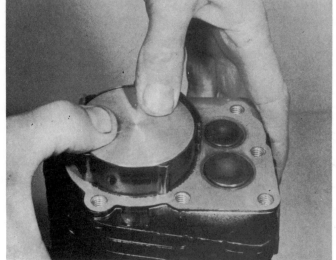

8

7 Fit the piston rings and assemble the gudgeon pin and connecting rod the same way round as noted during dismantling. Space the piston ring gaps at 120° from each other. The rings **must** be fitted the same way up and in the same grooves of the piston as when originally fitted. The photo shows the numbers cast on the web of the connecting rod facing upwards for clarity. These must face the flywheel end of the engine when installing the piston and connecting rod, i.e. the opposite way round to that shown in the photo.

8 Smear oil around the cylinder bore and on the crank throw journal. Using a piston ring clamp, fit the piston and connecting rod into the cylinder from the top. Do not scratch the bore with the big end as the connecting rod passes through. Press the piston firmly into the cylinder, sliding it out of the piston clamp as the rings enter the bore. If necessary, tap the piston gently with a piece of wood or a hammer handle, but stop and investigate any undue resistance.

9 Engage the connecting rod big end with the bearing journal on the crankshaft throw. Fit the big end cap with the oil groove in the bearing surface pointing towards the camshaft side of the engine. Secure the cap with the two bolts and tabwashers. Tighten the bolts firmly and bend the tabs tight against the bolt flats. Rotate the crankshaft to ensure free movement.

10 Turn the crankshaft to Top Dead Centre. Oil the cam follower stems and fit the followers into the same holes in the crankcase from which they were removed.

11 Smear some oil in the camshaft bearing and fit the camshaft into the crankcase.

12 Mesh the camshaft gear and the crankshaft gear with the index mark on the cam gear aligned with the marked tooth of the crankshaft gear.

13 Fit the oil pump body onto the eccentric drive on the camshaft, with the chamfered side of the hole in the body facing the cam gear. Remove the plunger, fill the body with oil and replace the plunger; this primes the pump for initial engine starting. The pump should be swung to the position shown in the photo so that the ball end of the plunger enters the slotted housing in the crankcase cover when the latter is fitted.

14 Fit the thrust shim onto the crankshaft.

15 Fit a paper gasket onto the crankcase.

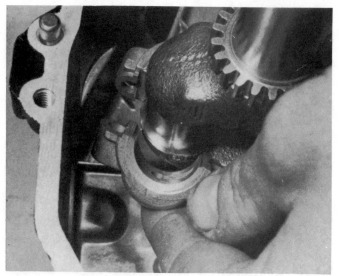

9

10

13

11

14

12

15

16 To fit a new oil seal for the main bearing in the crankcase cover, prise out the old seal with a screwdriver blade and fit the new seal in the same manner as previously described for the crankcase magneto bearing. Be careful not to damage the bore into which the seal fits or oil seepage may result.

17 Fit the engine speed governor plastic gear onto the stub shaft in the crankcase cover and retain it with a C-clip in the lower of the two grooves on the shaft. Check that the pivoting links move freely.

18 Fit the spool over the shaft, with the protrusion on the lower flange located into the space between the two pillars of one or other of the links; this ensures that the spool rotates with the gear. As the spool is fitted, check that the small lobe of each link is below the bottom flange of the spool and the large lobe is above the flange.

19 Secure the spool with a C-clip in the top groove of the shaft. Slide the spool up and down the range of movement between the two circlips and check that movement is free and that the two links pivot correctly. If movement is impeded, investigate the cause as the governor will not operate correctly and may allow the engine to overspeed. Worn or damaged parts are best rectified by fitting a complete new governor assembly.

20 Smear oil in the main bearing and camshaft bearing.

18

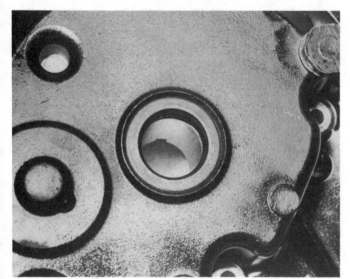

16

19

17

20

21 Check that the Woodruff key has been removed from the power take-off end of the crankshaft. Fit the crankcase cover carefully onto the crankshaft and slide it down onto the crankcase, guiding the oil pump plunger ball head into the slotted housing in the cover as the cover fits into place. Ensure that the governor gear teeth mesh correctly with the camshaft gear and that the crankcase cover locates correctly onto the dowels on the lip of the crankcase. Secure the cover with the six bolts, tightening them gradually in diagonal order to avoid distorting or cracking the cover.

22 Inspect the cam sleeve for signs of wear or grooving on the cam face. Check that the key machined in the bore of the sleeve is not worn, burred or otherwise damaged. Renew the sleeve if necessary.

23 Fit the cam sleeve onto the tapered end of the crankshaft, with the key on the sleeve aligned in the crankshaft groove and facing away from the engine.

24 Fit the contact breaker and coil unit assembly onto the engine. Make sure that the heel of the moving breaker point does not foul on the cam sleeve as the unit is offered into place; if this happens, pivot the breaker heel a little until the whole unit seats cleanly onto the lipped end of the crankcase.

23

21

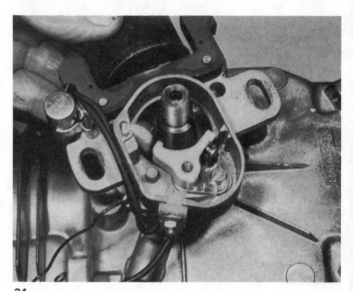

24

22

25 Secure the breaker and coil unit with the two bolts and flat washers, ensuring that the timing mark on the unit is aligned with the index mark on the crankcase, as shown by the arrow in the photo.

26 Turn the crankshaft until the heel of the moving point is resting on the highest point of the cam, then check with a feeler gauge that the breaker gap is 0.020 in (0.51 mm). If necessary, loosen the fixed point locking screw, move the point to the correct setting then tighten the locking screw. Put a small blob of grease on the heel of the moving point carrier. Re-check the setting, and readjust if necessary.

27 Fit the dust cover over the contact breaker housing and secure with the spring clip.

28 Fit the flywheel drive key into the groove in the tapered end of the crankshaft. The key must be free from shear marks or other damage; renew it if necessary.

29 Fit the flywheel onto the taper of the crankshaft with the slot aligned with the drive key.

25

28

26

29

27

30 Fit the rotating screen onto the threaded end of the crankshaft. Make sure that the three small grooves pressed into the bottom edge of the screen hub locate onto the nose of the three finger-shaped keys cast on the face of the flywheel. When the starter cord is pulled, the hub takes the recoil starter drive and transmits it to the engine through these keys. It is therefore essential that the hub is properly seated onto the keys and lies flush on the face of the flywheel.

31 If, on examination, the ratchets formed on the internal wall of the screen hub are found to be worn or burred, renew the screen. These ratchets are engaged by the starter pawl when the cord is pulled. Wear or damage in this area may cause the starter to slip and damage the pawl.

32 Secure the screen with the nut and domed washer (dome side up).

33 Fit a new cylinder head gasket.

34 Place the cylinder head on the cylinder.

30

34

31

35 Fit the five cylinder head bolts shown in the photo, but do not tighten them until the remaining three (which hold the cowl on) are fitted later.

36 Check the valve clearances after making sure the piston is at top dead centre on the compression stroke. The correct clearance for both valves is 0.10 in (0.25 mm). Check the disc valve on the inward facing side of the breather body. It should move freely and be undamaged. Fit a gasket to the valve chest and another to the outer face of the breather body, as shown above, then position the breather in the valve chest.

37 Rinse the breather filter in clean petrol, shake out the excess then fit the filter into the body.

38 Fit the cover onto the breather and secure with the two bolts.

32

35

36

37

38

39 Renew the carburettor float if it is perforated, damaged or shows signs of leakage (refer to Chapter 2 for leak testing). Examine the tip of the needle valve; if ridged, renew the valve. The synthetic rubber valve seat can also be renewed if worn. It can be pulled out of the hole in the carburettor body immediately above the needle valve by using a piece of hooked wire. The new seat should be smeared with oil, then pressed into the hole with a flat ended punch. Make sure that the grooved face enters the hole first, leaving the plain face outward for the needle valve to seat against.

40 The fixed jet need not be removed unless it is obviously dirty, in which case unscrew it carefully from the body. Check that the emulsion holes are clean by blowing through them, then screw the jet back into the body. **Do not** use a needle or hard wire to clean a dirty jet, because if a hole is damaged, accurate metering may be lost and the carburation upset. If blowing fails, use a thin nylon bristle, or something equally soft.

41 Place the float in position between the hinge lugs, ensuring that the needle valve enters the seat housing and seats correctly.

42 Push the pin through the lugs and float hinge bracket. Gently swing the float about the hinge and check that it moves freely. Do not apply force at the end of travel or the stop will be bent out of place and upset the fuel level.

39

40

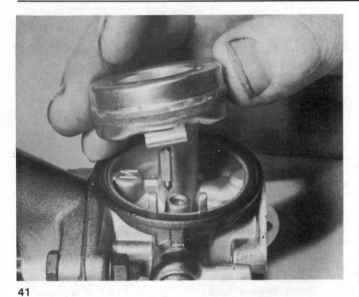

41

43

42

44

43 Check that the float bowl seal is not damaged or distorted and is seated properly in its groove. Fit a new one if necessary. Fit the float bowl, seating it correctly onto the seal.

44 Fit the bowl nut. Before tightening, ensure that the flat surface on the base of the bowl is positioned on the same side as the fuel inlet pipe, thus assuring full float travel.

45 Place a gasket on the inlet port.

46 Connect the throttle butterfly link to the hole in the tip of the governor lever while the carburettor and inlet manifold are still free. Connect the spring link to the second hole from the tip of the control lever on the engine control plate. Connect the spring on the end of this link to the third hole from the end of the governor lever.

47 Fit the inlet manifold and secure with the two shakeproof bolts.

48 Connect the magneto earthing lead to the spade connector on the engine control plate.

45

46

49 Attach the exhaust silencer to the exhaust port. Note that no gasket is provided.

50 Run the HT lead to the sparking plug inside the right hand hole for the cylinder head bolt. The cooling fin here is specially shortened to accommodate the lead.

51 Place the cowl onto the engine.

52 Fit the remaining three cylinder head bolts through the cowl, then tighten down all the cylinder head bolts a little at a time, in diagonally opposite rotation to prevent warping or cracking the cylinder head.

53 Fit the two bolts at the rear of the cowl near the fuel tank attachment slots.

54 Enter the air cleaner intake into the slot in the cowl and press it into the cut-out in the end of the slot.

55 Secure the air cleaner outlet elbow to the carburettor inlet with the two bolts.

47

49

48

50

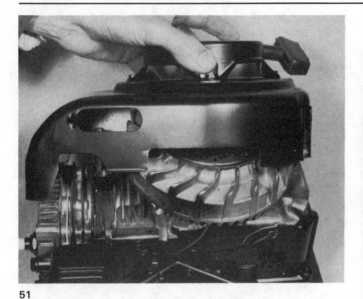

51

54

52

55

53

56 Fit the foam filter into the air cleaner housing. If the foam is dirty, wash it out thoroughly in a solvent solution, squeeze it out (but do not twist it) until it is dry, then oil it thoroughly with clean engine oil. Squeeze it vigorously to disperse the oil and remove the excess. Make sure that the housing is clean and dry. A foam filter that has gone solid or lost its resilience should be renewed, not forgetting to oil the new one.

57 Press the cover onto the housing until it snaps over the lip.

58 If the recoil starter assembly has been dismantled due to the need to replace a broken spring (the most usual cause of the cord failing to wind back onto the rewind housing after being pulled), proceed with the reassembly as follows:
    Fit the spring into the keeper. This is best achieved by hooking the outer end of the spring into the slot on the side of the keeper, then coiling the spring clockwise into the keeper, from outside to inside. Put a dab of grease in the keeper, place the keeper in the pulley and turn it until the two special tabs enter the slots under the pulley ribs.

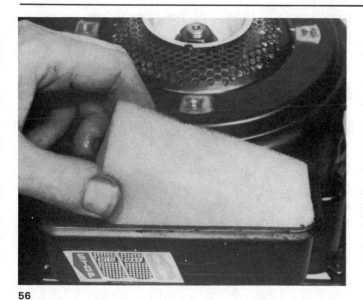

56

59

58

60

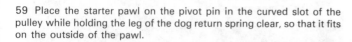

59 Place the starter pawl on the pivot pin in the curved slot of the pulley while holding the leg of the dog return spring clear, so that it fits on the outside of the pawl.

60 Place the pulley on the shaft in the starter housing. Turn the pulley anti-clockwise until the hook on the inner end of the recoil spring engages with the detent in the housing; a slight resistance can be felt when this happens.

61 Continue turning the pulley anti-clockwise until a positive return force is felt (about one turn should suffice) then hold the pulley at this tension. Wrap the cord anti-clockwise round the pulley until about six inches are left free. It may be necessary to ease the pulley up the shaft to do this, but not too far or the recoil spring may jump out of engagement.

61

62 Maintain pulley tension, thread the cord out through the hole in the starter housing, then through the handle and metal cleat. Tie a figure-of-eight knot in the cord and heat seal the end to prevent fraying. Press the cleat into the handle and release the pulley tension.

63 Place the coil spring in the recess in the housing shaft.

64 Fit the retainer hub over the dog pawl and tighten the cross head locking screw firmly. Pull the starter handle and check that the pawl emerges freely and that the starter turns freely. Relax the pull and check that the cord rewinds fully and positively.

65 Place the assembled starter on the cowl with the handle pointing towards the right hand end of the fuel tank, and secure it with the four screws.

66 Mount the fuel tank on the cowl by pressing the slotted mouldings on the fuel tank onto the carriers on the cowl.

64

62

65

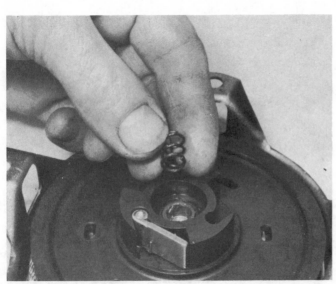

63

66

67 Connect the fuel pipe to the fuel tank and the carburettor; the pipe is a push fit at both ends. If the pipe is kinked, split (especially at the ends) or otherwise damaged, renew it.

68 Mount the engine on the deck and secure it from underneath with two bolts and one separate nut and bolt. The bolt is fitted in the hole near the oil filter hole and secured from underneath by the nut and washer.

69 Fit the Woodruff key in the slot in the crankshaft.

70 Fit the spacer on the crankshaft with the groove in the spacer aligned with the Woodruff key.

71 Position the cutter on the spigot on the end of the sleeve and secure with the bolt, collar and domed washer. Note that the blade must be fitted the correct way round, i.e. with the two cutting edges leading anti-clockwise rotation of the cutter, viewed from underneath the mower. The domed washer must be fitted with its concave face to the cutter.

69

67

68

71

70

72 Hold the blade using a thick rag to avoid injury from the cutting edge and tighten the blade firmly. Use a ring spanner, as a flat one is likely to slip and damage the head of the bolt. Try to tighten by pulling the spanner rather than pushing it, as injury to knuckles and fingers is much less likely if the spanner slips.

73 Connect the throttle cable to the carburettor and secure the sheath behind the clip. The sheath should be positioned to open the throttle butterfly to the full throttle position when the handle bar lever is at the fast run position (shown by the symbol of a hare). The cable sheath will probably show a mark where it was previously clamped; it should be reclamped in the same position.

74 If the adjustment setting of the needle valve has been lost, screw the needle very gently right in and stop as soon as it touches the seat. **Do not overtighten** or the valve seat and the needle will be damaged. Unscrew the needle $1\frac{1}{2}$ turns. This setting will enable the engine to be started and warmed up later for fine tuning of the needle valve.

75 Set the throttle stop until it barely touches the throttle butterfly lever, then screw it one turn clockwise. This will give sufficient throttle opening at idling for fine adjustment to be made later.

74

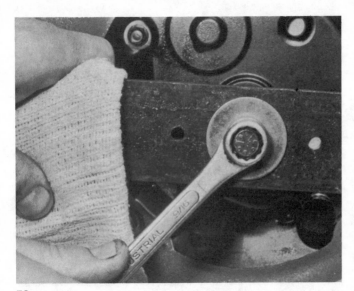

72

75

73

76 Set the stop screw to give a full travel position of the engine control lever which coincides with the full choke position of the choke butterfly, when the handle bar control lever is fully forward in the start position.

77 Check the condition of the height adjustment spring. The coils should be evenly spaced. A stretched, weakened or damaged spring increases the effort needed to adjust the height of the cut.

76

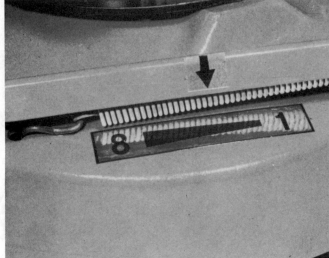

77

Technical data

Spark plug gap	0.028 in (0.6 mm to 0.7 mm)	Ring gap	0.007 to 0.017 in (0.18 to 0.43 mm)
Points gap	0.020 in (0.50 mm)	Fuel type	90 to 94 octane
Armature air gap	0.015 in (0.38 mm)		
Valve clearances: Inlet and exhaust	0.010 in (0.25 mm)		
Crankshaft end float	0.005 to 0.027 in (0.13 to 0.70 mm)		

Oil	Summer (Above 32°F)	Winter (Below 32°F)
	SAE 30 or, if not available, use SAE 10W 30.	SAE 5W20 or 5W30 or, if not available, use SAE 10W.

Victa Silver Streak

Chapter 5 Victa Silver Streak

Introduction

A smoother and neater appearance and more modern technical features distinguish the Victa Silver Streak rotary mower from its predecessor, the Professional. The well-proven Victa 160 cc 2-stroke engine is retained in virtually unchanged form, but with more up to date ancillaries (e.g. solid slate ignition) and neater engine fairing arrangements. The mower is hand-propelled and has four wheels that can be set to give the required cutting height by a single lever acting on all wheels simultaneously.

Grass cuttings are ejected by the cutter air flow into a removable grassbox at the rear of the mower. When the grassbox is removed a hinged deflector plate swings down to prevent particles and hard objects being ejected by the cutters and causing injury. The mower can be used with the grassbox removed and the deflector down when grass collection is not required, or when severe conditions clog the box.

A single lever on the handle bar controls the engine operation from stop (engine cut-off) through slow and fast running to the choke position (for cold starting).

The drive is not fitted with a disconnection device or an automatic brake and therefore the cutters will rotate at high speed all the time the engine is running. They will continue to rotate after engine switch-off until the engine becomes stationary. Therefore **do not put your hands or any implement under the casing when the engine is turning** or serious injury may result. Similarly, never lift the mower up or tilt it to investigate grass cutting blockages or for any other reason while the engine is still turning. Before touching the cutters or attempting to clear blockages, set the engine control lever to stop, wait for the engine to stop turning, then remove the lead from the plug. **Do not** raise the deflector plate when the engine is running, except momentarily to fit the grassbox. If difficulty is experienced with grass clogging, try raising the cutting height, as this improves the air flow through the mower and into the grassbox.

The two blades on the cutter disc are each mounted on a friction pivot to limit them from damage and protect the engine from shock loads if a solid object is struck. If this happens, stop the engine, remove the lead from the plug and gently tap the blades back to the correct position i.e. pointing radially outwards from the centre of the disc. Failure to correct blade position will unbalance the disc and lead to engine damage.

Dismantling

The hints and tips on engine overhauling in Chapter 2 should be read before starting to dismantle, as they will assist in a properly organised approach to both dismantling and reassembly.

1   Disconnect the plug lead.

2   Remove the cutter disc and its special square washer.

3   Remove the engine attachment nuts and shakeproof washers and lift the engine from the deck, taking care not to strain the throttle cable which cannot be disconnected at this stage.

4   Remove the drive dog sleeve from the crankshaft taper by taking the weight of the engine by the sleeve and hitting the end of the shaft with **a soft hammer**. If there is any difficulty, refit the nut and hit that, again using a soft hammer.

5   Pull the earth lead out of the hole on top of the rubber grommet alongside the carburettor intake.

6   Pull the grommet and the other length of earth lead from the carburettor. The engine can now be lifted away from the mower.

7   Pull the fuel pipe off the carburettor connector and remove the fairing and fuel tank from the engine.

8   Remove the cowl from the engine.

9   Twist the carburettor through 45 degrees to unlock it then pull it off the inlet manifold.

10 Remove the air intake trunking from the carburettor to reveal the throttle cable. The whole length of the cable from carburettor to handlebar lever is contained within the trunking.

11 Pull the press-fit cover off the top of the carburettor body, taking care that the coil spring under it doesn't fly out.

12 Free the shoulder under the cone-shaped tip of the plastic valve from the elongated hole in the diaphragm and remove the diaphragm, the spring under it and the plastic valve.

13 Lift the spider out of the carburettor.

14 Lift the throttle moulding off the stub shaft in the carburettor and disengage the nipple on the throttle cable from the recess in the moulding.

15 Disconnect the cable sheath from the slot in the carburettor intake. The carburettor can now be removed to complete its dismantling.

16 Free the two spring clips holding the exhaust silencer against the exhaust port and remove the silencer.

17 Remove the flywheel nut and domed washer and withdraw the flywheel from the crankshaft. Note that there is no taper on the crankshaft and no groove and key. A flat on the crankshaft mates with a matching flat in the flywheel hole to key the two together.

18 Remove the armature unit.

19 Remove the decompressor from the cylinder head, then the cylinder head from the cylinder studs.

20 Lift the cylinder off the studs.

21 Put a temporary mark on the gudgeon pin, piston and connecting rod to aid reassembly in the same position, then remove the piston.

22 Remove the four nuts, bolts and shakeproof washers holding the halves of the crankcase together.

23 Separate the crankcase and withdraw the crankshaft.

Reassembly

1   To fit a new oil seal in the flywheel half of the crankcase, prise out the old seal with a screwdriver blade but don't allow it to damage the bore into which the seal fits. Smear the new seal with oil and tap it gently into place in the hole, with the four slots facing outwards from the bearing.

2   To fit a new bearing, place it squarely on the hole and drive it in with a punch that touches the outer ring. **Do not** drive it in by striking the inner ring or the bearing may be seriously damaged. Keep hitting until the driver sounds solid.

3   Fit the spacer into place, aligned with the inner race.

4   Fit the second bearing in the same way as the first one.

5   Make sure that the bearings are driven right home so that there is no protrusion into the crankcase.

3

1

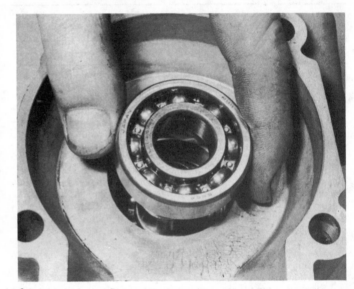

4

2

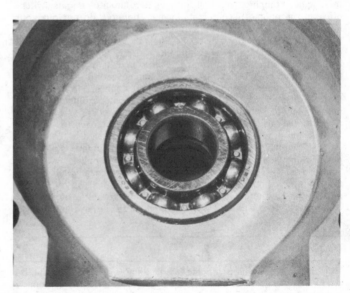

5

6   To fit a new oil seal in the drive half of the crankcase, repeat the procedure for the flywheel bearing seal.

7   Examine the crankshaft for obvious signs of damage or scores and check the fit of the big end on the crankpin. If the big end feels sloppy or was noisy with the engine running, a rear bearing and pin will have to be fitted professionally as this requires the use of a press and proper alignment checking facilities. The little end bearing should also be checked by sliding the gudgeon pin into it and rocking it. If sloppy, this bearing can be driven out and a new one fitted in a similar manner to the main bearings.

8   Enter the shorter end of the crankshaft into the larger half of the crankcase.

9   Apply non-hardening compound (e.g. RTV) to the crankcase joint face. Slide the smaller half of the crankcase onto the longer end of the crankshaft, and mate it firmly onto the larger half by tapping it with a wooden block. Do not rely on bolt tension to draw the halves together as this can cause a residual load on the bearings.

10 Fit, **but do not tighten,** the crankcase nuts, bolts and shakeproof washers. The bolts are fitted from the flywheel end of the engine.

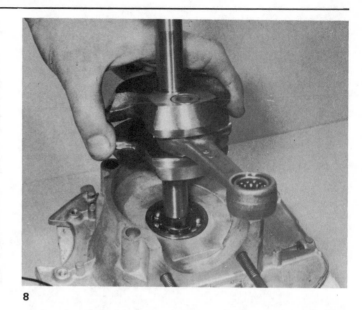
8

6

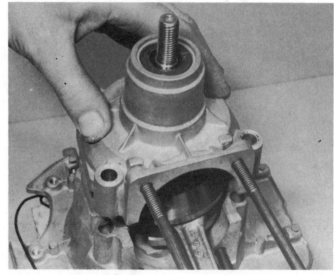
9

7

10

11 Fit new piston rings if necessary, ensuring that the gap coincides with the peg.

12 Fit the piston to the connecting rod the correct way round, as marked on the piston, gudgeon pin and connecting rod during dismantling.

13 Secure the gudgeon pin with the circlip.

14 Fit the thicker of the two cylinder gaskets onto the crankcase, using a new gasket.

15 Oil the piston rings lightly, fit the piston ring clamp, then ease the cylinder down the studs and onto the piston. **Do not** allow the piston rings to jam against the ports in the cylinder as the latter slides down. If any obstruction is felt, slide the cylinder up a little, re-oil the bore with heavy oil and try again. The piston ring pegs should be facing the inlet port if the piston and cylinder have been correctly assembled. Remove the piston ring clamp when the rings have successfully entered the bore.

13

11

14

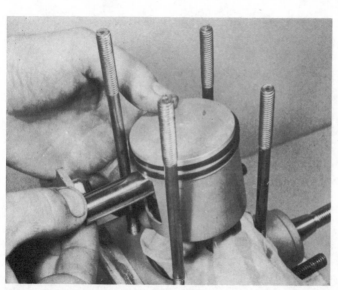

12

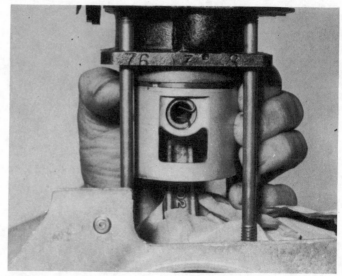

15

16 Fit a new cylinder head gasket. This is thinner than the gasket at the bottom of the cylinder.

17 Fit the cylinder head with the decompressor hole facing the flywheel side of the engine.

18 Fit the nuts and plain washers, tightening down just sufficiently for the cylinder to eliminate any stepping of the crankcase halves. Tighten the crankcase nuts and bolts firmly, then finally tighten diagonally opposite cylinder head nuts a little at a time to avoid warping or cracking the head. Rotate the crankshaft by hand to ensure that it turns freely.

19 Fit the armature and coil unit but do not tighten the bolts at this stage, or it may foul the flywheel when this is fitted later.

20 Press the earth lead connector onto the spade connection on the coil.

18

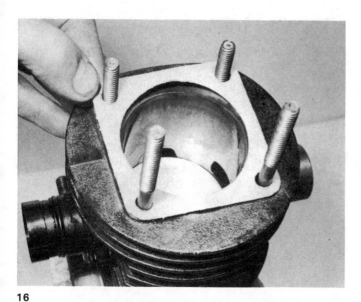

16

19

17

20

21 Fit the flywheel with the flat aligned with the flat on the crankshaft.

22 Fit the domed washer, dome side up. Thread the nut onto the crankshaft.

23 Line up the notch in the rim of the flywheel with the special hole in the crankcase. Insert a round bar into the hole and hold it in the notch to lock the flywheel, then tighten the nut. Check that the armature does not foul the flywheel then tighten its two bolts.

24 Blow through the tube into the decompressor and check that there is no resistance to air flow. Suck and check that the valve shuts positively and air cannot be sucked. If the changeover from shut to open is not prompt and positive, separate the housing, remove the valve retainer and spring and the valve itself. Clean the valve, check the diaphragm and renew if perforated. Clean the valve seat at the threaded end of the decompressor but do not scratch or damage it. Reassemble the decompressor and fit it to the threaded hole in the side of the cylinder head.

25 The order of assembly of the carburettor is illustrated by the photo.

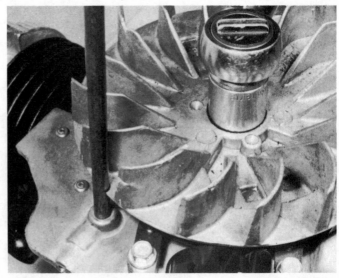
23

21

24

22

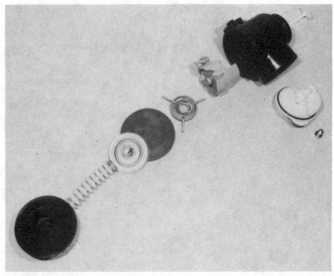
25

26 Insert the float valve into the housing moulded on the float chamber cover.

27 Fit the float to the float chamber cover by sliding the two hinge hooks onto the hinge pin.

28 Check that the cover O-ring is correctly seated and not damaged or distorted. Fit the cover assembly onto the float chamber.

29 Check that the filter mesh on the main jet body is clean and free from damage. To clean the filter, rinse in clean petrol and blow it, **do not** rub or brush it as it is fragile. If the mesh is torn, replace the main jet.

30 Align the float cover assembly with the carburettor body as shown in the photo and secure it with the main jet.

31 Place the brass washer on the carburettor body stub shaft.

32 Set the throttle lever to the stop position. Insert the cable into the carburettor body through the air intake, position the nipple through the aperture in the moulding as shown in the photo, then fit the shoulders on the sheath into the slots in the wall of the air intake.

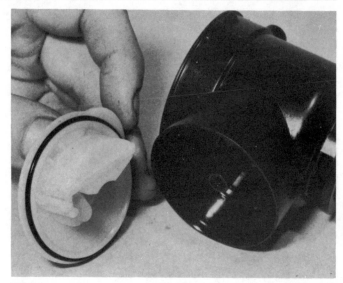

28

26

29

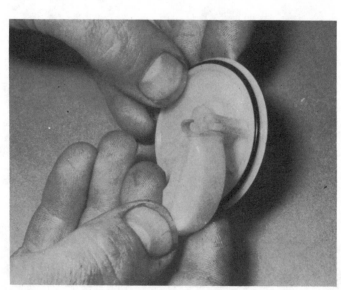

27

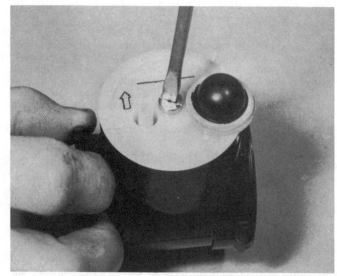

30

31

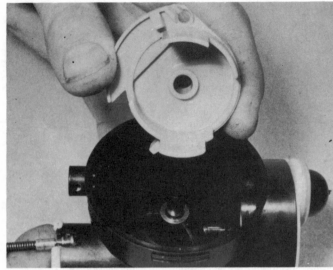

33a

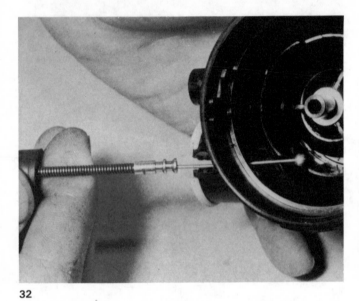

32

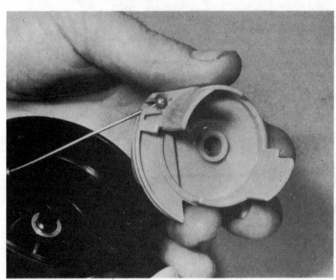

33b

33 With the nipple recess in the throttle moulding positioned vertically above the cable nipple (see photo 33a) place the moulding on the stub shaft, rotating it a little either way until the recess fits onto the nipple. The nipple seats as shown in photo 33b, but **do not try** to assemble as shown in photo 33b, because the cable will always straighten and jump out as soon as the moulding is turned face down towards the stub shaft.

34 Place the moulded spider face down onto the spigot of the throttle moulding, with the arms of the spider resting in the cut-outs.

35 Pass the stem of the valve up through the centre of the valve body.

36 Hold the valve so that the shoulder at the end is well clear of the spider. Fit the shorter of the two coil springs onto the spider.

37 Fit the diaphragm, numbered side down, onto the tip of the valve stem.

38 Move the diaphragm sideways so that the small end of the elongated hole engages under the shoulder on the valve stem.

34

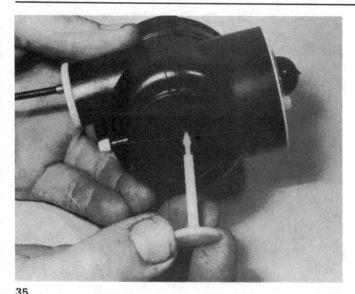

35

36

37

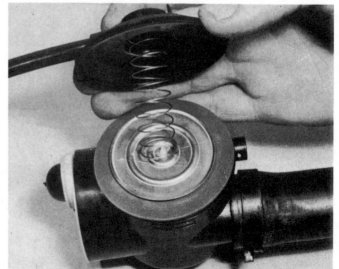

38

39 Place one end of the longer spring into the cover recess, the other end on the centre of the diaphragm, then press the cover onto the body. Ensure that it is firmly snapped on all the way round. Connect the intake trunking to the carburettor inlet.

40 Fit the exhaust gasket, dome side in, to the silencer.

41 Secure the silencer to the exhaust port spigot by the two spring clips. These locate on the cylinder studs and the lip of the silencer.

42 Fit the cowl onto the engine, with the exhaust silencer steady bracket underneath it.

43 Secure the cowl with the four bolts, and the two dome nuts that screw onto the two extended cylinder head studs.

44 Inspect the fuel pipe filter for damage and cleanliness. Rinse it in clean petrol and blow through the pipe with the tap turned on in order to clean it; do not brush or rub it as the mesh is fragile and may be damaged. Fit the pipe into the fuel tank.

45 Place the foam rubber ring on the neck of the fuel tank. Fit the fuel tank to the plastic engine cover and retain it with the filler cap.

39

40

43

41

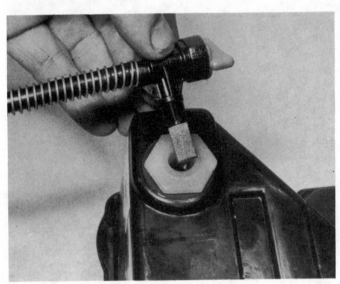

44

42

45

46 Fit the engine to the deck and secure it with the nuts and shakeproof washers.

47 Insert the cut-out fitting on the end of the ignition earthing lead into the housing on the carburettor.

48 Set the throttle lever to the Run position. Push the grommet onto the carburettor housing. Push the shorting pin down through the hole in the side of the grommet, through the hole in the carburettor housing, and finally through the second hole on the other side of the grommet. If the pin is not properly home, the engine may not be cut-off when the control lever is set to stop.

49 Connect the pipe from the decompressor to the push-on fitting on the side of the carburettor intake.

50 Fit the waved lock washer on the engine inlet port spigot, place the carburettor on the spigot with the locking slots in the carburettor intake correctly aligned on the spigot. Push the carburettor against the lock washer and twist it 45 degrees to the locked position (see photo 50b).

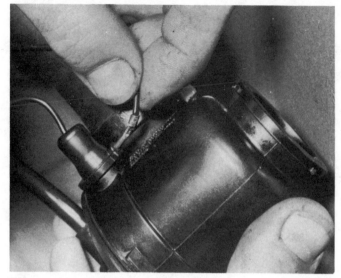

48

46

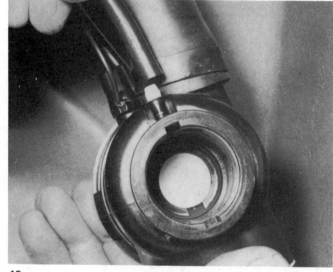

49

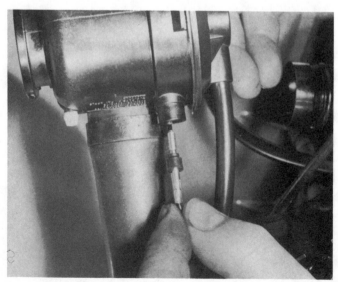

47

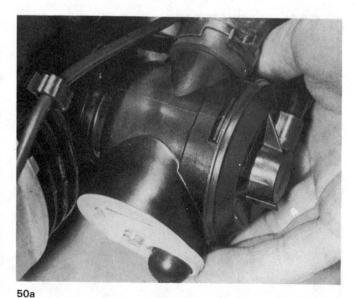

50a

50b

52

51 Hook the fuel tank cradle into the slot in the rear of the engine cowling.

52 Fit the engine cover and fuel tank, threading the starter handle up through the slot in the cover.

53 Fit the grill to the fairing.

54 Connect the fuel pipe to the push-on connector on the float chamber cover.

55 Fit the drive dog sleeve onto the crankshaft taper.

56 Place the cutter disc over the shoulder of the drive dog.

57 Fit the square nut onto the drive dog. Note that the washer is marked with the side which must face the nut.

58 Fit the nut. Use a round bar placed in the special hole in the crank to stop the cutter disc from turning and tighten the nut.

53

51

54

55

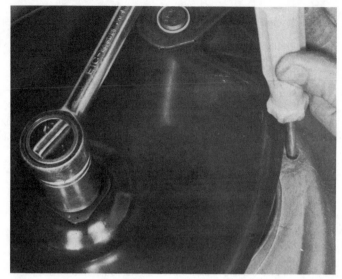

58

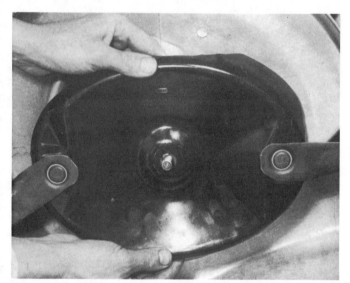

56

Recoil Starter Repair

To renew either a pull cord or a broken recoil spring, the starter unit must be removed from the engine. First remove the engine fairing to gain access to the starter unit, then remove the three cross-head screws that secure the starter to the crankcase. The centre screw is much larger than the two corner screws, and passes right through the central bearing sleeve before screwing into the crankcase. Dismantle the starter as follows:-

1   Pull out just over 1 ft of the starter cord, hold the pulley tension by hand and unwind the cord.
2   Allow the pulley to unwind slowly until all tension is freed.
3   Pull out the central bearing sleeve.
4   Pull the large spring clip out from between the gear and the pulley.
5   Lift the clip locating plate from the side of the housing.
6   Lift the pulley and gear assembly out of the housing.
7   Remove the broken recoil spring.

To reassemble the recoil starter proceed as follows:

(1)   Hook the outer end of the spring onto the spring post and wind the spring anti-clockwise into the housing, coiling from outside to inside.

(2)   If a new cord is required, anchor it in the cleft between the two pulley flanges.

57

1

(3) Thread the cord through the hole in the housing, from inside to outside, then fit the handle to the cord.

(4) Fit the pulley and gear assembly onto the rim in the centre of the housing, turning it clockwise slightly to engage the spring hook with the slot in the pulley hub. Place the clip locating plate in position, overlapping the pulley. Insert the two screws through the holes in the housing, one passing through the hole in the clip locating plate. Stretch an elastic band temporarily over the screws to hold them and the clip locating plate in position.

(5) Press the clip onto the hub between the pulley and the gear.

(6) One leg of the clip should be located in the gap in the locating plate. The other leg should be resting on the flat of the plate near the screw.

(7) Turn the pulley clockwise three turns to tension it, then, while holding the tension, wind any surplus cord onto the pulley.

(8) Fit the bearing sleeve into the pulley hub. Gently pull the handle and check that when it is released, it returns positively taking the handle back firmly against the housing.

5

3

6

4

8

(9) While holding the gear close to the pulley, fit the starter housing onto the crankcase, carefully screwing the two screws held by the elastic band a few turns into the threads. Snip the elastic band and withdraw it through the gap between the starter housing and the crankcase. Fit the long screw through the bearing sleeve then tighten all three screws.

(10) Fit the engine fairing as described previously in this chapter.

9

Technical Data

Spark plug gap	0.025 in (0.63 mm)
Points gap	0.020 in (0.50 mm)
Piston ring gap (new rings)	0.006 in (0.15 mm)
Fuel mixture	1 part of any good brand of 2-stroke oil to 25 parts of petrol

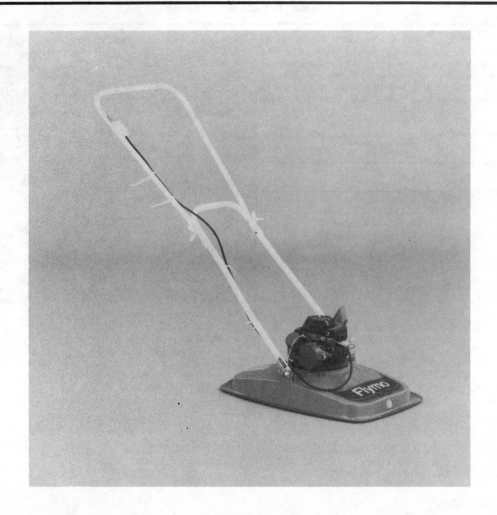

Flymo TL Micromo

Chapter 6 Flymo TL Micromo

Introduction

With a weight of only 7 kg (15.4 lbs) the Flymo TL Micromo is the lightest of the current range of Flymo petrol-engined lawnmowers. It is powered by a Kawasaki 22.6 cc 2-stroke engine and has a 12 inch wide cut. An impeller immediately above the cutter blade creates a cushion of air on which the mower floats clear of the ground as soon as the engine is started. Having no wheels for support, the mower must be carried to the place of work or storage, hence the importance of it being as light in weight as possible. It is designed to hang vertically for storage on a wall hook.

Grass cuttings are fine mulched and ejected back to the lawn, thus no grassbox is provided.

Like all rotary mowers, the Micromo is dangerous if misused. **Never put the hands or any tool or implement near the cutters when the engine is turning.** An air cushion mower should never be left unattended with the engine running as there is virtually no resistance to its running away. If you must leave it, stop the engine. When stopping the engine, tilt the mower sideways towards you, then move the start/stop control to the stop position and wait for the engine to stop turning. Failure to tilt the machine will cause the blade to cut a ring on the lawn as the air cushion dissipates and the mower settles. Do not pull the mower over chippings or other lose objects with the engine running; stop the engine then carry the mower. **Never carry the mower with the engine running** as you risk serious injury.

Because of the fixed aerodynamic effect of the air cushion on the cutting height of the blades above the ground, cutting height is altered by fitting the appropriate number of the spacers provided between the blade and the impeller. Two spacers are available; when both are fitted the blades are lowest for shortest cut. When none are fitted, the blades are highest and give the longest cut.

Read the maker's operating instructions thoroughly before attempting to use the machine until its use has become familiar. This advice is more important for air cushion mowers because their operating principle is so different from more conventional rotary mowers.

Dismantling

Read the hints and tips in Chapter 2 before starting to dismantle. They will assist towards a properly organised and methodical approach to dismantling and reassembly.

1   Disconnect the plug lead.
2   Remove the cutter blade, blade spacer(s) and the impeller disc.
3   Withdraw the fluted bush from the crankshaft.
4   Disconnect the engine cut-off lead from the handle bar cable.
5   Remove the three cross-head screws recessed into the underside of the deck and lift the engine off the deck.
6   Remove the four cross-head screws securing the circular adapter casting to the engine and remove the adapter.
7   Disconnect the fuel pipe from the tank and remove the tank.
8   Remove the carburetter and the plastic manifold to which it is attached.
9   Remove the exhaust silencer box.
10 Remove the screen from the recoil starter housing.
11 Remove the recoil starter.
12 Remove the cast impeller casing from the engine, pulling apart the ignition earth lead connector in the transparent sleeve before lifting the casing away, complete with the ignition armature and coil unit mounted inside it.
13 Remove the cowl from the cylinder head. Keep the fibre packing washer between the cowl and the cylinder head.
14 Remove the sparking plug.
15 Remove the flywheel. This will require a simple extractor and three 6 mm bolts which screw into the holes provided in the flywheel. The extractor can easily be made up from a piece of flat steel plate, with three holes spaced to align with the flywheel holes as shown below.

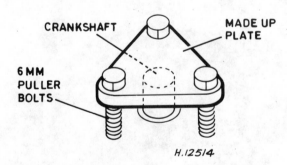

H.12514

Preload the bolts evenly, then strike the top of the plate in line with the crankshaft to free the flywheel from the taper. Remove the key from the crankshaft groove.

16 Remove the cover from the contact breaker points. Remove the points assembly and the condenser (the silver tube which lies outside the cover).
17 Remove the cylinder and gasket from the crankcase.

18 Mark the end of the gudgeon pin and piston for reassembly the same way round as when removed. Remove the gudgeon pin and piston from the connecting rod.

19 Remove the roller bearing cage from the little end of the connecting rod, taking care not to lose any of the rollers.

20 Unscrew the driveshaft from the taper on the crankshaft. To loosen the driveshaft, place a round bar of suitable size in the little end of the connecting rod, jam it with two blocks of wood (see reassembly instructions) to stop the crankshaft turning, then use a spanner on the two flats on the driveshaft.

21 Remove the four cross-head screws holding the crankcase halves together and separate the crankcase. A tap with a wooden mallet or block of hard wood may be necessary to part them.

22 Remove the crankshaft and connecting rod from the crankcase half.

23 Remove the bronze thrust washer and the square thrust plate from the smaller half of the crankcase. The crankshaft cannot be separated to replace the big end bearing without special alignment equipment to reassemble it. If the big end is worn or noisy in operation, take the assembly to a specialist for repair.

Reassembly

1   To fit a new roller bearing in the drive side of the crankcase, the seal must first be removed. Use a screwdriver to prise it out as described in the earlier chapters. Drive out the bearing using a piece of round bar or an old box spanner of slightly smaller diameter than the outer track of the bearing. Drive it evenly, from the outside of the crankcase towards the interior. Do not let it tilt as it is driven out or the hole in the crankcase will be damaged. Oil the new bearing and drive it in evenly until it is fully home against the internal shoulder.

2   To fit a new seal, oil it and tap it gently into place against the bearing. It should be fitted with the sharp edge of the lip pointing inwards.

3   Follow the same procedure for the flywheel ball bearing in the larger half of the crankcase as for the roller bearing in the smaller half, removing the oil seal first.

4   Fit a new oil seal in the same way as for the smaller half of the crankcase.

5   The order of assembly of the crankshaft components is shown in photo.

2

3

1

5

6 Fit the square thrust plate into the recess. Fit the bronze thrust washer onto the crankshaft. Oil the crankshaft and fit it into the crankcase half.

7 Apply gasket sealing compound of the non-setting type to the joint face of one half of the crankcase. Oil the other end of the crankshaft and slide it into the bearing in the larger crankcase half. Ensure that the dowels enter the holes correctly as the two halves mate together.

8 Fit the cross-head screws with a spring washer first and then a flat washer, then screw them into the crankcase. Tighten firmly but be careful not to strip the threads in the crankcase casting.

9 Screw the driveshaft onto the unkeyed end of the crankshaft.

10 To tighten the driveshaft, place a round bar with protective tape on it into the little end bearing of the connecting rod, block it with wood, then tighten the driveshaft.

8

6

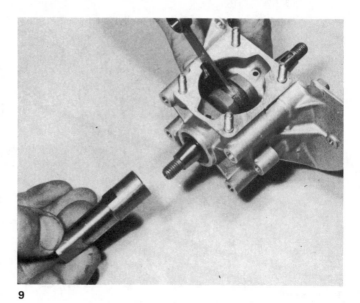

9

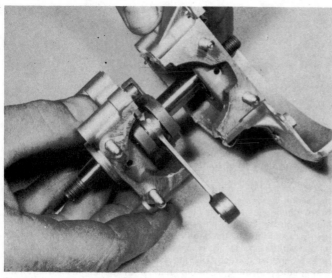

7

10

11 Fit new piston rings if necessary, as described in Chapter 2, ensuring that the gaps and pegs coincide.

12 Oil the small end needle roller bearing and fit it into the connecting rod. Cover the opening into the crankcase while doing this to prevent dirt falling in.

13 The piston has an E and an arrow on the crown. These must be facing the exhaust port side of the engine when the piston is fitted to the connecting rod.

14 Oil the gudgeon pin, fit the piston onto the connecting rod and slide the gudgeon pin in. It should be fitted the same way round as marked when it was removed.

15 Fit the circlips into the piston, ensuring that they seat properly into their grooves.

13

11

14

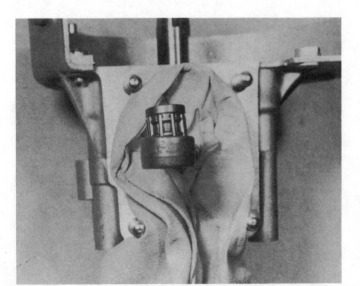

12

16 Place a cylinder gasket onto the crankcase. Make sure that the cut-outs in the gasket coincide with the crankcase ports.

17 Oil the piston and the bore of the cylinder. Slide the cylinder onto the piston very carefully, easing the rings into the lead-in chamfer at the beginning of the bore. If the piston is obstructed by the rings ledging on the cylinder ports, **do not** force it, but rotate the cylinder gently to and fro until the rings ease past the ports. Secure the cylinder with the nuts and spring washers. Make sure that the cylinder has been assembled correctly i.e. with the exhaust port (seen in photo with a long stud projecting from it) pointing in the direction shown. Rotate the crankshaft to ensure free movement.

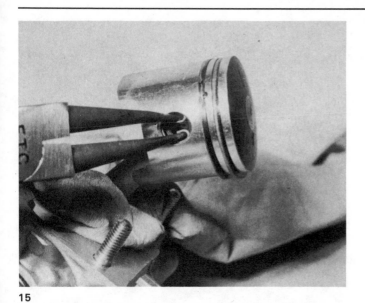

15

18 Fit the contact breaker assembly.

19 Screw the breaker baseplate cross-head screw into place but do not tighten at this stage.

20 Fit the condenser and connect the tab on the end of the lead under the screw and washer on the heel of the moving point.

21 Turn the crankshaft until the heel of the moving point is on the top of the cam i.e. points fully open. Set the gap between the points to 0.015 in (0.38 mm) then tighten the baseplate screw. Fit the small clip over the lead near the base of the cylinder.

16

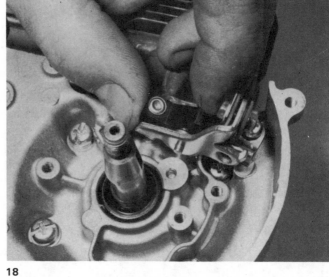

18

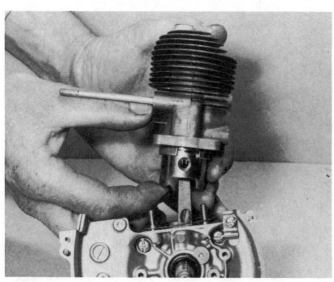

17

19

20

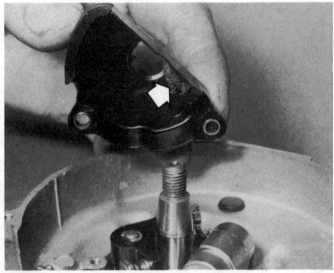

22

21

23

22 Impregnate the lubricating pad in the contact breaker cover with a light grease and fit the cover.

23 Fit the key into the crankshaft slot and fit the flywheel.

24 Secure the flywheel with the nut and spring washer. Use a spanner on the flats at the drive end of the crankshaft and tighten the flywheel nut firmly.

25 Hold the impeller casing near the flywheel, connect the ignition earth lead spade and lug connector and slide the transparent protective sleeve over the connector.

26 Locate the impeller casing on the crankcase dowels and secure it with the cross-head screws.

24

25

27

26

28

27 Place a gasket on the face of the inlet port.

28 Position the heat shield on the inlet port gasket. Place the other gasket on the outer face of the heat shield. The inner and outer gaskets are the same.

29 Fit the plastic manifold block and secure it with the two cross-head screws and spring washers. Note that the small hole in the manifold is at the bottom.

30 Check that the main jet O-ring is not damaged or distorted and that it is seated properly in the groove. Screw the jet into the carburettor body and tighten.

29

30

32

31 Insert the coil spring into the hole in the middle of the carburettor body. Engage the needle valve shoulder in the slot in the flat lever. Insert the needle valve into the valve seat and, at the same time, locate the pivot pin of the lever into the two grooves in the carburettor casting.

32 Tighten the cross-head screw down onto the pivot pin to secure the needle valve assembly in position against the pressure of the coil spring.

33 Fit the diaphragm onto the two dowels on the carburettor body.

34 Fit the cover plate onto the dowels and secure it to the carburettor body with the four screws and spring washers.

33

31

34

35 Insert the priming valve into the carburettor body.

36 Place the priming lever in position on the carburettor mounting lug, with its return spring located in the hole in the cover plate, and its forked lever engaged in the shoulder of the priming valve. Secure it to the lug with the screw.

37 Check the condition of the priming pump diaphragm. If it is cockled, torn or has become hard, especially at the flap valves, renew it. Place the gasket on the housing and then place the diaphragm on the gasket with the flaps over the horse shoe shaped chambers.

38 Fit the other half of the housing and secure it with the two screws and spring washers.

39 Locate the two bosses of the priming pump into the ports in the carburettor and secure it with the two screws and spring washers.

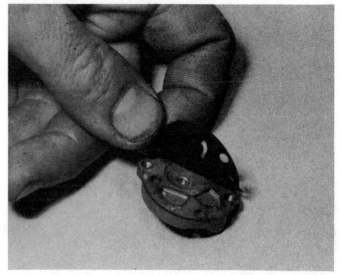

37

35

38

36

40 Check the mixture adjusting needle for wear or damage. Screw it into the carburettor gently until it seats, then back it off 1½ turns. This will provide a datum to fine-tune the setting later when the engine can be started.

41 Fit the main jet assembly into the carburettor body. The setting is locked by the serrated collar.

42 Secure the main jet housing with the two screws and spring washers.

39

42

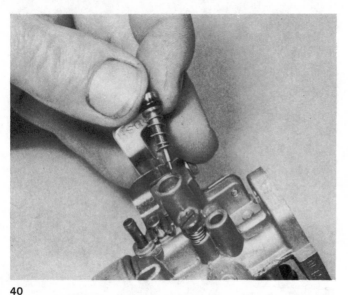

40

43 Check the operation of the choke lever. It should move without obstruction, but is slightly stiff to prevent vibration moving it from the position set. The choke operates in two positions, full choke and half choke, by obstructing the carburettor inlet. Full choke is used for a cold start, and half choke for the engine warm-up period.

44 Wash the air cleaner foam element in solvent, squeeze it dry and install it in the housing.

45 Fit the air cleaner cover so that the inlet mesh will face downward when the carburettor is installed on the engine. If the cover is dirty, clean it in solvent before fitting it.

46 Secure the cover by tightening the cross-head screw on the collar.

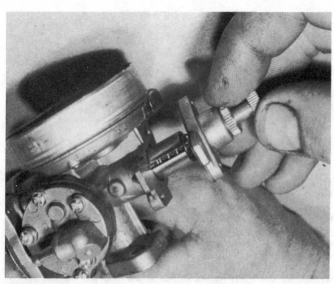

41

43

47 Place the heat shield gasket on the carburettor manifold studs so that it curves out over the crankcase.

48 Fit the carburettor onto the manifold studs and secure the two nuts, with a flat washer under one nut and the pipe support clip under the other.

44

45

46

47

48

49 Fit the priming pump tube through the support clip and push it onto the inlet pipe on the priming pump. Note that the arrow on the bulb points towards the carburettor.

50 Place the fibre spacer over the hole on top of the cylinder head, fit the cowling onto it and secure with the two screws and flat washers.

51 Place a gasket on the exhaust port studs and fit the exhaust silencer onto the studs.

52 Secure the silencer with the two nuts, flat washers and spring washers. Fit the flat washer under the spring washer.

53 Fit the fuel tank to the crankcase with the three screws and spring washers.

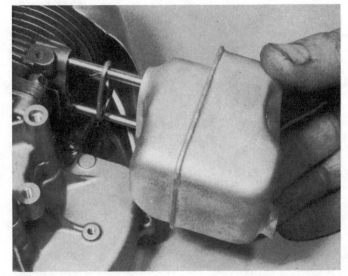

51

49

52

50

53

54 Fit the inner seal, ball bearing and outer seal into the adapter casting, and secure with the circlip.

55 Fit the large washer into the bearing recess.

56 Place the felt seal on the washer.

57 Fit the cover plate and return with the three countersunk screws, but do not tighten them at this stage to allow the felt seal to centre on the crankshaft.

58 Place the adapter casting on the engine with the arrow pointing towards the top of the cylinder.

56

54

55

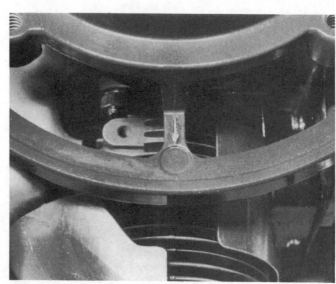

57

58

59 Secure the adapter casting to the engine with the four screws.

60 Tighten the felt seal cover plate.

61 The fuel feed components are shown in photo. Clean the felt on the weight at the end of the tube by washing it in clean petrol. Wash the brass mesh strainer in clean petrol, taking particular care that no dirt is caught in it. The felt can be removed if required by pulling the weight off the tube, then sliding the felt off the weight. When removing the strainer from the rubber housing, note which way round it is as it must be replaced the same way.

62 Fit the strainer into the rubber housing the same way round as when it was removed.

63 Insert the weight and feed pipe into the fuel tank outlet.

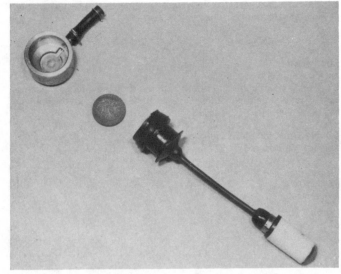

61

59

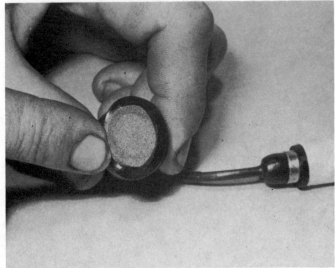

62

60

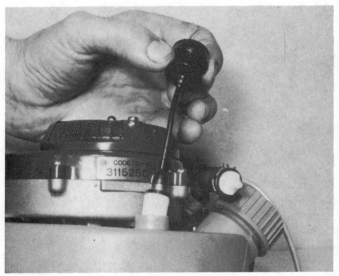

63

64 Press the rubber housing onto the tank outlet. Press the cap over the rubber housing.

65 Connect the fuel feed cap to the primer pump rubber bulb assembly with the short tube and two spring clips.

66 Lift the engine into position on the deck with the cylinder pointing forwards and secure it from underneath with the three screws and flat washers.

67 Connect the ignition cut-off switch lead from the handle bar to the spade connector on the lead from the impeller casing. Slide the transparent sleeve over it.

68 Fit the angled plate to the impeller casing, securing the tag on the remaining lead from the handle bar cut-off switch under one of the screws.

66

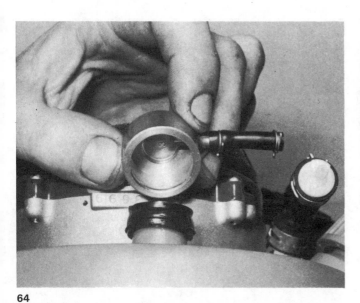

64

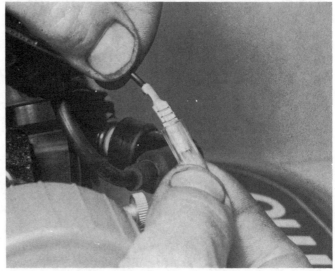

67

65

68

69 Place the fluted bush on the crankshaft.

70 Fit the impeller disc onto the fluted bush.

71 Fit the number of blade spacers to suit the required depth of cut.

72 Secure the blade to the crankshaft with the angled tips pointing downwards.

73 Hold the blade with a rag to prevent injury from the sharp cutting edge and tighten the bolt firmly.

71

69

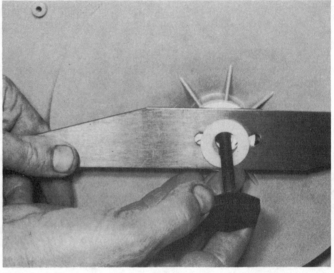

72

70

73

74 The handle bar can be removed, for convenience if transporting the mower or working on it, by pulling out the spring clip and R-clip from each of the two attachments, and disengaging the handle bar from the up-lock. Before removing the handle bar, remember to disconnect the ignition cut-off leads from the engine leads.

75 Strict observance of the warning notice is essential if serious injury is to be avoided. When started, the engine runs up immediately to normal operating speed and has no slow run setting. It is therefore immediately supported on the air cushion which offers virtually no resistance to movement of the mower. **Never,** therefore, leave it unattended while the engine is running.

Recoil Starter Repair

To renew either a pull cord or a broken recoil spring, the starter unit must be removed from the impeller casing and dismantled as follows:-
1 Remove the mesh screen.
2 Remove the starter unit.
3 Remove the chromium plated dome locknut from the internal slotted screw.
4 Remove the slotted screw.
5 Carefully raise the pulley just enough to unwind the cord and release pulley tension. If the spring is broken the pulley can be lifted straight out as there will be no tension. Lift off the fibre disc. To reassemble the recoil starter, proceed as follows:-

(1)   Fit the recoil spring into the housing so that it coils in an anti-clockwise direction. Hook the outer end through the slot in the rim of the housing.

(2)   Ensure that the pulley faces and the central bore are clean. Smear them with a little light grease.

(3)   Place the fibre disc on the pulley.

(4)   Fit the pulley onto the stub shaft in the housing, rotating it gently anti-clockwise as it is fitted until the slot in the pulley hub engages the hook at the inner end of the spring.

(5)   Turn the pulley anti-clockwise three turns to pretension it and hold it in this position.

(6)   Wind the cord anti-clockwise onto the pulley, easing it up slightly if necessary to ease the cord in between the pulley flanges. Do not ease it too high or it will disengage from the spring.

(7)   When all the slack cord is wrapped onto the pulley, push the cord fairlead into the slot in the edge of the housing.

74

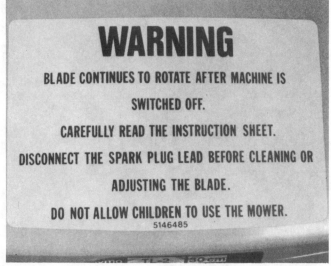

WARNING

BLADE CONTINUES TO ROTATE AFTER MACHINE IS
SWITCHED OFF.
CAREFULLY READ THE INSTRUCTION SHEET.
DISCONNECT THE SPARK PLUG LEAD BEFORE CLEANING OR
ADJUSTING THE BLADE.
DO NOT ALLOW CHILDREN TO USE THE MOWER.
5146485

75

1

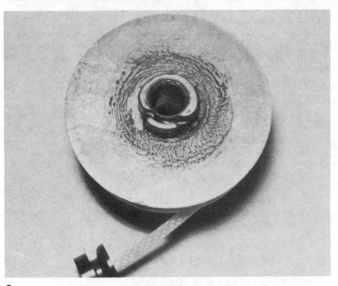

2

(8)   Fit the slotted screw into the centre of the stub shaft, tighten it then release the pulley. Pull the handle and release it; check for free movement and a positive return action.

(9)   Fit the locknut and tighten it.

(10) Examine the pawls for wear and freedom of movement. Check that the pawl springs are unbroken and the coils unstretched. The serrations on the pawls and on the central hub of the pulley must not be worn smooth. Renew worn or damaged parts.

3

9

4

10

(11) Fit the starter unit onto the impeller casing, carefully easing the pulley hub into engagement with the pawls. Pull the handle slightly to assist engagement, if necessary. Secure the starter unit with the two screws.

(12) Pull the starter handle and check for correct operation. Fit the mesh screen with the two screws.

12

11

Technical Data

Spark plug gap	0.024 to 0.027 in (0.6 to 0.7 mm)
Points gap	0.015 in (0.38 mm)
Piston ring gap	0.003 in (0.08 mm)
Fuel mixture	1 part oil to 25 parts petrol.

Use only Flymo 2-stroke Mower Oil with 2-star petrol (90 octane minimum). **Do not** use premix 2-stroke fuel from garage pumps and **do not** use multigrade oil.

Honda HR 17

Chapter 7 Honda HR17

Introduction

In most respects the Honda HR17 follows conventional hand-propelled rotary mower design, but with one or two important innovations. It is powered by a 76 cc, 4-stroke, Honda G100 engine and has four wheels, each separately adjustable by its own lever for height of cut. Grass cuttings are ejected at the rear into a removable grass bag. A spring-loaded discharge guard hinges down as the grassbox is removed, thus giving protection against particles and objects ejected by the cutter. It also allows the mower to be operated without the grass bag fitted if grass collection is not required.

Two important features designed to improve safety are a drive disconnection clutch and a brake which automatically stops cutter rotation as soon as the drive is disconnected. A 'deadman's handle' type of lever on the handle bar is spring-loaded towards the drive disconnected position. When the handle is in this position, the roto-stop brake is applied to stop the cutters turning. By pushing the handle forward in the palm of the hand and then grasping the handle bar to hold the handle against it, the Roto-stop brake is released and simultaneously the drive engaged. The engine is constant-speed controlled at the normal operating speed and has no throttle lever.

The engine cut-off switch has two 'off' positions, one on either side of the central 'on' position. This makes emergency stops quicker and less prone to fumbling.

Dismantling

The hints and tips on overhauling given in Chapter 2 should be read before starting to dismantle. They are intended to make the approach to dismantling and reassembly more orderly and methodical.

1 Disconnect the plug lead. Drain the oil from the engine.
2 Remove the recoil starter from the fan shroud.
3 Remove the air cleaner.
4 Remove the fan shroud, disconnecting the fuel pipe before lifting the shroud away.
5 Lift the collars from the studs on which the shroud was mounted.
6 Remove the cutter. Be prepared to take the spring pressure as the central bolt is loosened.
7 Remove the exhaust muffler cover, bottom plate, deflector pipe and gasket.
8 Remove the roto-stop link and spring.
9 Disconnect the ignition cut-off lever from the handle bar lead.
10 Remove the engine holding nuts and bolts and lift the engine from the deck.

11 Pull the breather tube off the connection on the air cleaner housing.
12 Disconnect the automatic choke link.
13 Disconnect the governor link and spring, noting which holes the link and spring connect into.
14 Disconnect the petrol pipe from the carburettor.
15 Remove the carburettor.
16 Remove the carburettor joint plate with the studs in it, the two gaskets and the plastic insulator from the cylinder inlet port.
17 Remove the automatic choke bimetallic strip.
18 Remove the tappet cover complete with the fuel pipe supported by it, the gasket and the separator box.
19 Remove the flywheel nut.
20 Remove the recoil starter drive dish, the screen grid and the plastic impeller.
21 Remove the flywheel from the crankshaft taper and remove the key from the groove in the taper. To free the flywheel, replace the flywheel nut until it is flush with the end of the crankshaft threads. Hold the weight of the engine by the flywheel. Using a soft hammer or a normal hammer and a block of soft metal, strike the nut flush on the face. This should break the grip of the taper. The nut and flywheel can then be removed. Some assistance will be needed for this operation. This method is a useful alternative when a proper flywheel puller is not available, but take great care not to damage the threads. If the hammer or block are not held square while striking the nut, the crankshaft can be bent or the end broken off.
22 Remove the cover from the contact breaker assembly and remove the assembly.
23 Remove the coil assembly.
24 Remove the cylinder head.
25 Remove the crankcase flange bolts and split the oil pan from the crankcase.
26 With the crankshaft on TDC of the compression stroke to relieve the camshaft load, withdraw the camshaft and the two thrust washers. Note that the larger washer is at the outer end.
27 Mark the cam followers for reassembly in the same holes then remove them.
28 Remove the valves
29 Remove the big end cap, separate the connecting rod from the crankpin and withdraw the crankshaft.
30 Remove the piston and connecting rod through the bottom of the bore and into the crankcase. This avoids the risk of scratching the cylinder bore with the connecting rod. Remove the piston from the connecting rod, noting carefully which way round it fitted, and which way round the gudgeon pin fitted.
31 Withdraw the crankshaft complete with the main ball bearing.

Reassembly

1   The correct assembly relationship of the piston and connecting rod is shown in the photo.

2   If the original piston rings are being refitted they must be placed in the same grooves and the same way up as originally fitted. The step on the middle ring must be uppermost. After fitting the piston rings, assemble the piston to the connecting rod. The gudgeon pin must be the same way round as when removed. Secure it with the circlip.

3   Fit the thrust washer on the governor shaft. If the oil slinger or governor weight holder wheel are worn or damaged, renew them.

4   Fit the governor wheel on the stub shaft with one of the weights fitted.

5   Secure the wheel with a C-clip. Ensure that the C-clip is properly seated in the groove on the shaft.

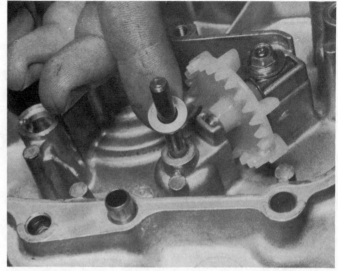

3

1

4

2

5

6   Fit the slider onto the shaft with the flange located between the prongs of the weight.

7   Position the other weight on the wheel with its two prongs located either side of the slider flange.

8   Secure the weight with the split pin.

9   Renew the oil seal in the flywheel bearing of the crankcase if necessary. The part numbers and slots in the face of the seal should face outwards. Prise out the old seal with a screwdriver as described previously for other engines. Smear the new seal with oil and tap gently into place.

10   Renew the oil seal in the oil pan if necessary, in the same manner as for the flywheel bearing.

8

6

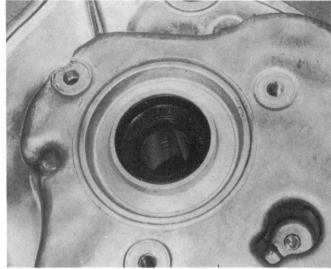

9

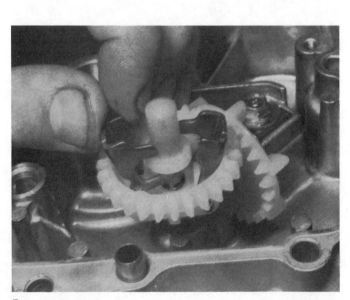

7

10

11 Smear the piston with oil then carefully enter it into the bore of the cylinder from the crankcase end. The lead-in chamfer of the bore will guide the piston rings into the cylinder. The offset big end should be facing away from the governor side of the crankcase.

12 Smear the crankshaft with oil to ease it through the seal. Insert it into the crankcase, complete with the flywheel ball bearing. Tap it gently home with a soft hammer until the bearing seats against the shoulder in the crankcase housing. Smear the crankpin with oil.

13 Engage the big end of the crankpin, fit the big end cap, two bolts, two lockwashers and the flat washer.

14 Tighten the bolts firmly. Turn the crankshaft to ensure free rotation.

15 Smear the valve followers with oil and insert them into the same holes from which they were removed.

16 The small thrust washer fits at the lower end of the camshaft and the larger one to the upper end. Position the smaller one on the camshaft bearing in the crankcase.

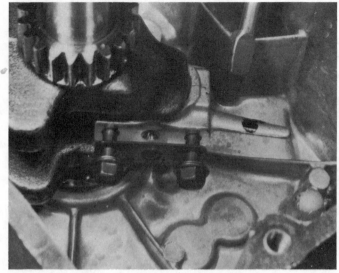

13

11

15

12

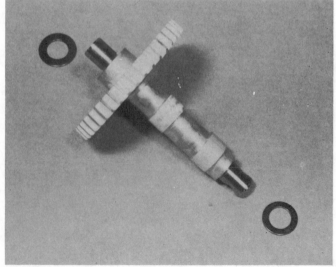

16

17 Turn the crankshaft until the timing mark on the cam gear will coincide with the mark on the camshaft. Fit the camshaft and mesh the gear with the timing mark aligned with the crankshaft cam gear mark.

18 Fit the large thrust washer to the top of the camshaft.

19 The correct position of the two timing marks is shown in the photo.

20 Fit the thrust washer onto the crankshaft.

21 Fit the two hollow dowels into the crankcase.

22 Fit a new crankcase gasket. Do not use jointing compound.

23 Fit the oil chamber gasket and cover plate.

24 Oil the crankshaft and fit the oil pan onto it. Slide the oil pan down the crankshaft, locate it on the hollow dowels then mate it onto the crankcase face.

19

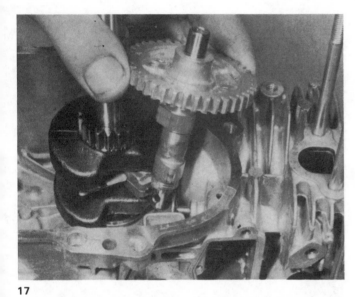
17

20

18

21

22

25 Fit the six crankcase flange bolts and tighten a little at a time diagonally to avoid cracking or distorting the oil pan.

26 The valve components are shown in the photo. The large end of the oval hole in the collar allows the full width of the valve stem through. The collar can then be slid sideways so that the narrow end of the oval fits under the shoulder on the valve stem, thus locking the valve and spring together. The adjuster cap is fitted onto the tip of the valve stem after reassembly of the valve. Note that the inlet valve is larger than the exhaust valve.

27 To fit the valves, place the coil spring in the valve chest with the collar under, dished side of the collar upward.

28 Oil the valve stem and slide it down through the guide and the collar. Lever the collar up with a screwdriver while pressing the valve down, slide the collar sideways until it engages under the shoulder of the valve stem, then release the leverage.

29 To fit the valve clearance adjuster cap, lever the valve up with the screwdriver again until the head of the valve is well clear of the seat. Slide an open spanner under the head to hold the valve open.

23

25

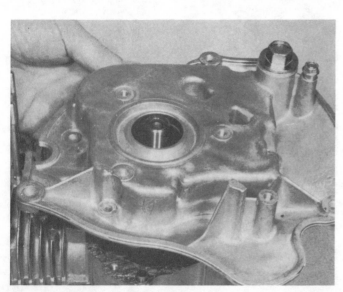

24

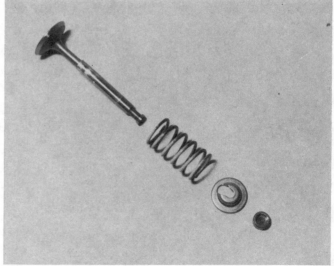

26

27

28

29

30 Fit the cap onto the valve stem and withdraw the spanner gently, so as not to damage the valve seat or cylinder head face.

31 Check the valve clearance with a feeler gauge. Both valves should have a clearance of 0.002 to 0.004 in (0.05 to 0.10 mm). An adjuster cap of the approximate length is obtainable to achieve this clearance. Failing this, the head of the cap can be lapped to achieve the required clearance. The cap must be held square while lapping. If the valves need grinding in, the clearances will also need attention.

32 Fit the separator box into the valve chest.

33 Fit the gasket and tappet cover, complete with the fuel pipe which is supported on it.

34 Using a new cylinder head gasket, fit the cylinder head.

30

31

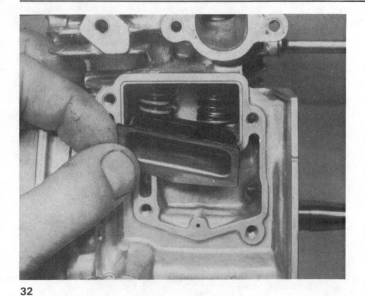

32

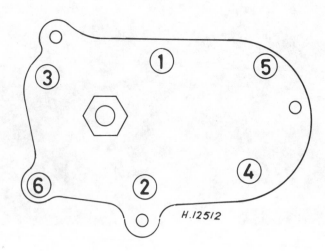

33

35 Tighten the two nuts and four bolts a little at a time in rotation, to the pattern shown in the photo. Even tightening is essential to avoid cylinder head distortion. See accompanying illustration.

36 Fit the shroud.

37 Place the coil assembly in position on the two mounting bosses, with the small electrical lead grommet pressed into the slot in the crankcase web.

38 Fit the condenser with its mounting plate hole on the coil assembly hole, and secure the condenser and coil assembly with the two set screws (seen in the photo 39). Press the condenser lead into the slot in the grommet containing the coil assembly lead.

39 Fit the contact breaker assembly with the peg on the base plate in the plain hole near the crankshaft oil seal.

34

35

36

39

37

40 Set the contact breaker gap to 0.012 to 0.016 in (0.3 to 0.4 mm). This will give the correct ignition timing of 20 deg. before T.D.C. If this timing is not achieved within the recommended range of adjustment, the points are worn and new ones must be fitted. Tighten the cross-head screw when the adjustment is correct. Connect the two leads (one from the condenser, the other from the coil unit) to the nut and bolt on the contact breaker base plate. The tags are to be on the outside of the insulating washer.

41 Impregnate the breaker oil pad with light grease. Fit a gasket on the breaker housing.

42 Fit the cover over the contact breaker assembly.

43 Place the Woodruff key in the slot in the crankshaft.

44 Fit the flywheel. Ensure that it engages properly with the key in the crankshaft.

45 Fit and tighten the flywheel nut.

46 Place the plastic impeller on the flywheel. Make sure that the three pegs in the underside locates in the matching holes in the flywheel.

38

40

41

44

42

45

43

46

47 Place the screen grid on the impeller with the locating hole over the peg on the impeller.

48 Position the recoil starter drive dish on the screen grid. Fit and tighten the three bolts.

49 Thoroughly clean the main jet (the smallest of the components shown in the photo) by rinsing in petrol and blowing through it. Do not use a pin in the jet or the metered orifice will be damaged. Similarly clean the main nozzle (shown next to the main jet). Again, do not poke pins into the metering holes. Insert the main nozzle into the carburettor body, then secure the main jet into the same hole and tighten gently.

50 Check the needle valve for wear and ridging. Check the spring (which pushes the head onto the valve seat) for weakness. Replace the whole valve if defects are found. The valve slides into a slot in the float and is easily removable. Place the float and valve assembly on the carburettor body.

51 Insert the float hinge pin.

49

47

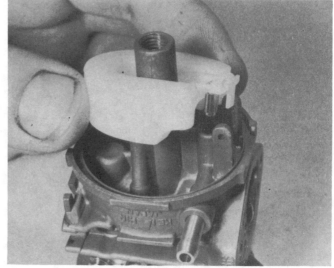

50

48

51

52 Check that the float chamber gasket is correctly seated and is not damaged or distorted. Renew if necessary. Fit the float chamber in position.

53 Secure the float chamber with the set bolt and washer.

54 Check the pilot jet screw for a damaged or bent needle tip. Screw it in gently until it seats, then unscrew $1\frac{3}{4}$ turns. This setting can be fine tuned later when the engine is started.

55 Prise off the lid of the automatic choke housing. Move the choke lever gently away from its stop and check that it returns freely to the stop under spring pressure. The spring can be replaced by undoing the choke butterfly and withdrawing the spindle from the choke housing. Press the snap fit cover back onto the housing.

56 Fit the gasket to the inlet port. Install the plastic insulator on the port, with the tongue inside the port.

54

52

55

53

56

57 Place the triangular gasket on the insulator. Fit the carburettor joint plate and secure it with the two cross-head screws.

58 Place the gasket on the joint plate.

59 Pass the governor link through the coils of the throttle return spring and connect the link and the spring to the hole in the tip of the governor lever. The coils of the spring must be at the governor lever end of the link. Slide the carburettor onto the studs of the joint plate and connect the other end of the link, and the throttle return spring, into the throttle butterfly lever. Do not secure the carburettor at this stage.

60 Ease the carburettor up the studs sufficiently to fit the bimetal strip and its bolt. Tighten the bimetallic strip in place.

61 Hook one end of the choke rod into the choke housing. Connect the other, sharply hooked, end into the bimetallic strip and secure it with the lock pin.

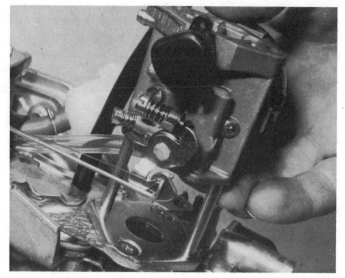

59

57

60

58

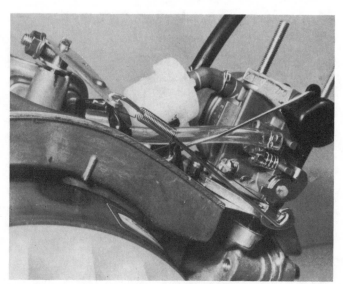

61

62 Fit the fuel pipe assembly, with the filter situated near the carburettor. Secure the fuel tap with the cross-head screw. Fit the governor lever return spring.

63 Fit the air cleaner gasket and the packing to the carburettor inlet.

64 Attach the air cleaner housing to the carburettor joint plate studs and push the breather pipe on to the housing connector.

65 Press the ball track into the recess in the oil pan.

66 Place the muffler gasket on the engine deck.

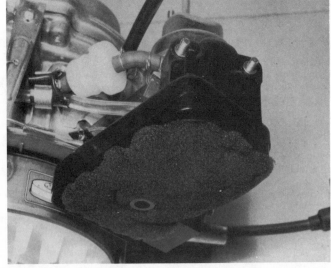

64

62

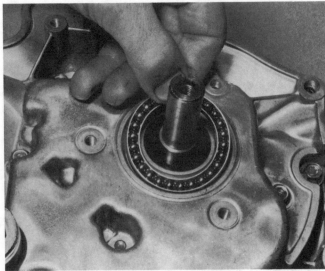

65

63

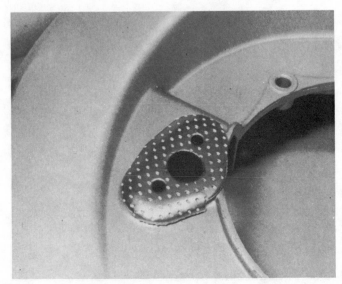

66

67 Position the engine on the deck, entering the exhaust port studs down through the muffler gasket. Fit the three engine bolts and screw the nuts onto them from under the deck.

68 Tighten the engine holding nuts and bolts firmly.

69 Position the muffler on the two studs under the deck.

70 Fit the muffler bottom plate.

71 Fit the muffler cover onto the bottom plate, fit the two nuts onto the studs and tighten them.

69

67

70

68

71

72 Fit the deflector pipe over the muffler exit hole on the deck, pass the long flange bolt down through the deflector pipe and muffler assembly, fit the nut and tighten it. Engage the Roto-stop cable nipple in the lever, then hook the roto-stop spring to the lever.

73 Line the lever up with the threaded hole, fit the bolt through it, place the flat washer on the bolt then screw the bolt into the threaded hole and tighten it.

74 Lever the other end of the spring over the head of the bolt in the crankcase.

75 Fit the ball control plate with the gap in its rim engaged with the roto-stop lever.

76 Place the ball retainer on the ball control plate.

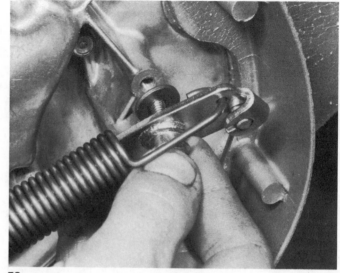
73

72a

74

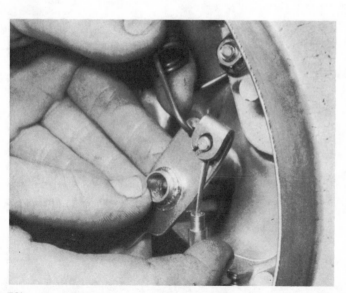
72b

75

76

77b

77 Place the Roto-stop disc on the ball control plate (photo 77a) ...

... secure it with the three bolts (photo 77b)

78 Insert the key into the slot in the crankshaft (photo 78a) ...

... then fit the drive disc onto the crankshaft (photo 78b).

79 Place the driven disc on the drive disc, (photo 79a) ...

... and the clutch spring on the driven disc. Insert the bolt into the blade holder and locate the boss of the blade holder in the clutch spring (photo 79b).

80 Press the blade holder against the clutch spring, locate the three bushes in the blade holder on the three pegs of the driven disc and screw the bolt into the crankshaft.

81 Tighten the bolt firmly.

78a

77a

78b

79a

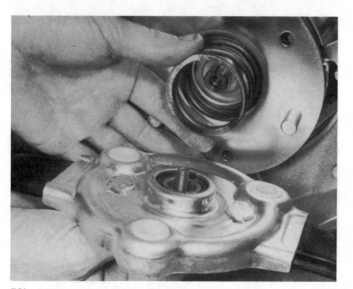

79b

81

82 Connect the ignition shorting lead from the engine to the lead on the handle bar. Connect the HT lead on the sparking plug.

83 Place the flat washer and collar on each shroud mounting stud.

84 Install the shroud complete with the fuel tank on the studs. Secure it with the long bolt through the fuel tank. Connect the fuel pipe to the tank with the spring clip.

85 If the recoil starter requires no attention, position it on the mounting studs and fit and tighten the cap nuts. If repair is necessary, do not install the starter at this stage but refer to Recoil Starter Repair later in this chapter.

86 Replace the handle column cover.

87 Adjust the Rotor-stop brake cable as necessary to brake the cutter blade when the handle is released. Free play at the tip of the lever should be 0.2 to 0.4 in (5 to 10 mm).

88 Clean the air cleaner foam element by rinsing in solvent, **not petrol**, and squeeze it dry. Do not wring it as this crushes and tears the foam. Saturate the element in clean oil, squeeze out the excess and install the element in the house. Fit the cover.

80

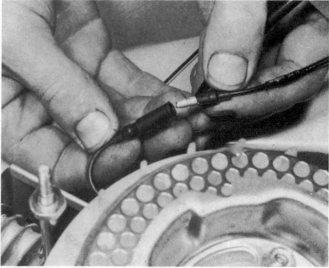

82

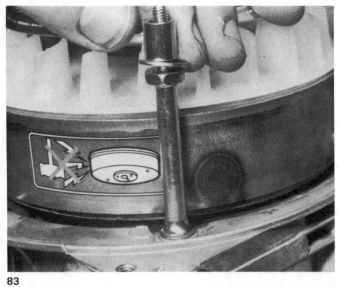

83

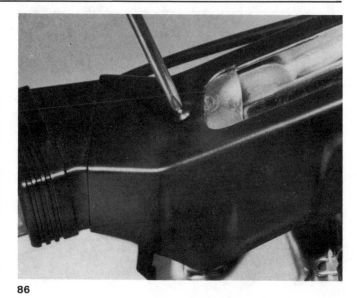

86

84

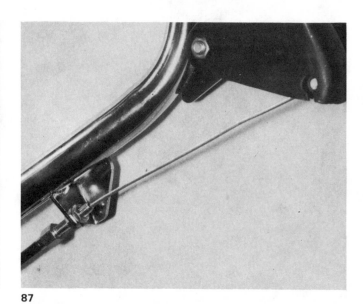

87

85

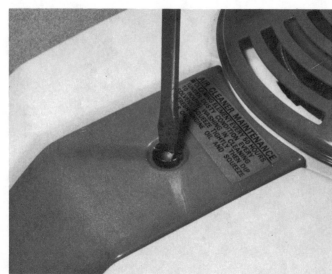

88

Recoil Starter Repair

To fit a new cord or recoil spring, the starter housing must be removed from the shroud, and dismantled. With the housing removed, proceed as follows:-

(1)　To release pulley tension, pull out the starting handle 3 turns of the pulley, trap the cord in the pulley notch, then let the pulley unwind 3 turns, taking the cord with it.

(2)　Remove the central bolt and lift off the friction plate complete with friction spring.

(3)　Check the ratchet and ratchet spring for unobstructed movement and positive return of the ratchet. Renew the ratchet spring if necessary.

(4)　Lift off the pulley. Remove the recoil spring if broken. Fit a new cord to the pulley if necessary.

4

1

5

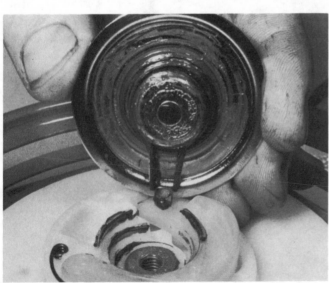

2

(5)　To fit a new spring, hook the outer edge end into the slot in the housing, then wind the spring anti-clockwise into the housing, working from outside in towards the centre. Apply grease to the spring coils.

(6)　Replace the pulley onto the centre stub shaft. Turn it anti-clockwise until it seats right down and engages with the hook on the inner end of the spring.

(7)　Fit the friction plate and spring onto the pulley with the two legs of the spring on either side of the lug on the ratchet.

(8)　Fit the central bolt.

(9)　Trap the cord in the pulley notch, wind the pulley and cord 3 turns anti-clockwise. Hold the pulley, free the cord from the notch and release the pulley.

(10)　Pull the cord and release it to ensure full movement and a positive return action.

(11)　Install the housing on the studs and secure it with the cap nuts. Pull the handle and check that engagement of the ratchet feels right and that the ratchet does not jump out.

Technical Data

Spark plug gap	0.020 to 0.030 in (0.6 to 0.7 mm)	Piston ring side clearance (standard)	*Top Ring* 0.0010 to 0.0022 in (0.025 to 0.055 mm)
Points gap	0.012 to 0.016 in (0.3 to 0.4 mm)	(service limit)	0.004 in (0.10 mm) *Second and Oil Rings*
Valve clearances: Inlet and exhaust (standard)	0.002 to 0.004 in (0.04 to 0.10 mm)	(standard)	0.0004 to 0.0016 in (0.010 to 0.040 mm)
Piston ring gap (standard)	0.006 to 0.014 in (0.15 to 0.35 mm)	(service limit)	0.004 in (0.10 mm)
(wear limit)	0.04 in (1.0 mm)	Oil	SAE 10W-30 or 10W-40 all temps. SAE40 above 30°C SAE30 15 to 30°C SAE20 or 20W 0 to 15°C SAE10 below 0°C

Honda HR 194

Chapter 8 Honda HR 194

Introduction

The Honda HR 194 is a four-wheeled, self-propelled rotary mower. It is powered by a GXV120, 118 cc 4-stroke engine which has breakerless transistor magneto ignition and also features overhead valves.

A single lever on the handle bar controls engine operation from stop (engine ignition cut-off) through low and high speed to the choke position (for cold starting).

A full-width handle bar lever operates the self-propel drive clutch when pushed and gripped against the handle bar. As soon as it is released the self-propel drive is disengaged and the mower stops. A smaller lever on the right-hand side of the handle bar is pushed to free a Roto-stop brake on the cutter and engage the drive to the cutter. This lever is automatically operated by the self-propel lever so that both the drive and the cutters are operated by one action. The Roto-stop lever has a push button on it which allows the self-propel lever to be pushed without automatically operating the cutter Roto-stop lever, thus permitting mower travel without cutter operation.

The self-drive transmission provides two forward speeds, under the control of a lever beside the throttle lever.

Cutting height is adjusted by a separate lever at each wheel. The handle bars can also be adjusted for height.

Grass is ejected at the rear into a removable grass bag. A discharge guard hinges down over the opening when the grass bag has been removed. It is spring-loaded and must be raised slightly to allow removal of the grass bag, and lifted completely to allow fitting of the grass bag. The mower can be operated without a grass bag in severe conditions or when grass collection is not required.

Dismantling

Refer to the hints and tips on overhauling in Chapter 2 before starting to dismantle. The information given will ensure a methodical and properly organised approach to the job. To dismantle the mower, proceed as follows.

1 Disconnect the plug lead. Drain the oil from the engine.
2 Remove the handle bars. Be careful not to damage or kink the control cables.
3 Loosen the handle bar locknuts of the Roto-stop cable and unscrew the adjuster to release tension in the cable.
4 Free the throttle cable from the carburettor.
5 Remove the cutter blade.
6 Remove the cover panel from the transmission. Remove the plastic cover from the drive shaft.
7 Remove the engine mounting bolts.
8 Slide the engine forward so that the transmission drive shaft slides off the serrations on the final drive unit shaft.
9 Undo the two nuts securing the air cleaner duct to the carburettor. Remove the bolt securing the air cleaner to the engine. Remove the air cleaner complete with the engine breather pipe.
10 Remove the fuel filler cap.

11 Remove the engine cover.
12 Remove the petrol tank from the engine. Disconnect the fuel pipe from the tank, withdrawing the filter from the tank connector as the pipe is removed. Handle the filter with great care as it is very fragile.
13 Remove the clutch central bolt. Withdraw the cover plate, spring, clutch plate and pressure plate.
14 Make a careful note of the positions of all springs and links to assist reassembly in the same holes.
15 Remove the linkage mounting plate from the engine.
16 Remove the carburettor and the plastic insulator plate. Remove the float chamber, float and needle valve for inspection. Dismantle the fuel tap.
17 Remove the ignition unit.
18 Remove the exhaust muffler assembly (consisting of a shield, muffler box and gasket).
19 Remove the central bolt holding the brake assembly together and lift off the Roto-stop brake components.
20 Remove the Woodruff key from the crankshaft.
21 Unscrew the three flange bolts and springs from the brake housing and lift off the housing.
22 Lift the ball retainer from the ball control plate.
23 Remove the Roto-stop return springs and lift off the ball control plate.
24 Remove the circular spacer from the crankshaft.
25 As a precaution, make a permanent mark on the governor lever and the shaft. If the lever ever becomes loose it is then easy to set it to the original datum.
26 Remove the flywheel nut from the crankshaft and lift off the rotating screen/starter hub, and the flywheel and impeller. Remove the key from the crankshaft taper.
27 Remove the overhead valve cover and gasket.
28 Remove the cylinder head complete with valves.
29 Remove the crankcase cover. Make a careful note of where the bolts of differing lengths fit to assist reassembly.
30 Mark the big end of the connecting rod and the cap before removing the latter, as the cap will fit both ways. It must be reassembled the same way round as originally fitted.
31 Withdraw the piston and connecting rod through the top of the cylinder, taking care not to scratch the bore.
32 Withdraw the camshaft and then the crankshaft. Pull the R shaped clip off the drive shaft. Withdraw the drive shaft from the crankcase cover. To remove and dismantle the final drive unit, remove the right-hand rear wheel.
33 Remove the height adjusting plate pivot bolts from both back wheels.
34 Remove the torque reacting bracket.
35 Lift the back axle clear.
36 Disconnect the speed change cable and the drive engage cable.
37 Remove the protector plate from the axle.
38 Remove the final drive case bolts, split the two halves of the casing and remove the internal components.
Note: If any difficulty is experienced in carrying out these instructions, refer to the photographs in the reassembly instructions that follow. Used in the reverse sequence, these photographs indicate the steps in dismantling and will help to identify the components mentioned above.

Reassembly

1   The governor components are shown in the photo. Fit the C-clip into the groove in the shaft; it is easier to do this at this stage.

2   Slide the carrier wheel onto the governor shaft from the end with the slot in it. The weights on the wheel must be facing away from the slot. Fit the smaller washer onto the shaft after the wheel. With the wheel and washer as far onto the shaft as they will go, fit the shaft into the crankcase cover. The slot in the shaft mates onto a key machined in the cover casting. Fit the shaft clamp with the fork in the end engaged on the peg on the cover. (The gear seen in the photo will not have been fitted at this stage). Place the larger washer in the shaft, then fit the slider onto the shaft with its flange engaged between the weights.

3   Insert the drive shaft into the crankcase cover.

4   The gear and its fixing components are shown in the phot.

5   Fit the washer with the smaller hole onto the shaft, so that it will be between the first bearing and the gear. Slide the shaft into the gear.

3

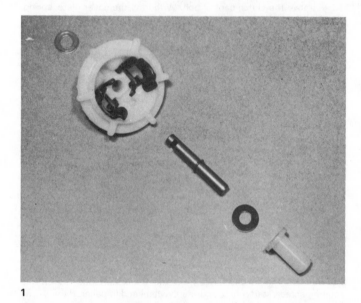

1

4

2

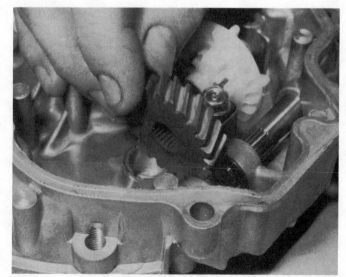

5

6   Fit the washer with the larger hole onto the end of the shaft then push the shaft into the second bearing.

7   Insert the clip **between the gear and the washer.** Fit the straight leg of the clip into the hole in the shaft and press until it clicks fully home.

8   Fit a new oil seal to the crankcase cover bearing if necessary, in the same way as described previously for other engines.

9   The drive shaft is also fitted with an oil seal. If necessary, renew the seal before fitting the drive shaft.

10   Fit a new oil seal to the crankcase flywheel bearing if necessary.

8

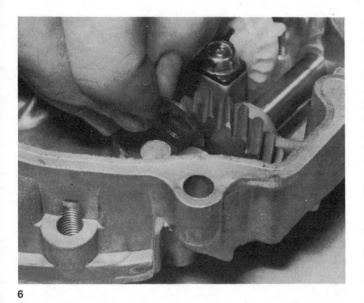

6

9

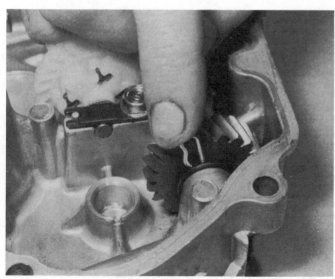

7

10

11 The flywheel bearing in the crankcase is a ball bearing. To renew it, remove the oil seal and drive the old bearing in towards the crankcase interior. Fit the new bearing from the interior. Drive it into the housing with a piece of tube **that bears on the outer race only.** If the ball cage or the inner race are struck, the bearing will be damaged. Keep the bearing square as it is driven into the casting.

12 Smear a little oil on the crankshaft parallel portion at the tapered end. Insert the crankshaft into the crankcase bearing.

13 Assemble the connecting rod to the piston the same way round as when removed i.e the oil hole on the same side as the arrow on the piston crown. If the gudgeon pin has been removed, fit it in the conventional manner, the same way round as when it was removed, and replace the circlips securely.

14 Fit a piston ring clamp to the piston. Oil the bore of the cylinder and insert the piston into it, taking care not to scratch the bore with the connecting rod. Press the piston out of the clamp and into the bore. Tap it gently with a piece of wood if necessary, but stop and investigate any obstruction or the piston rings may break. The arrow on the piston crown must be pointing towards the ohv push rod hole in the casting.

13

11

14

12

15 Invert the engine and oil the crank pin, engage the big end on it and **fit the big end cap the same way round as marked when dismantling.** Note that the cap will fit the wrong way round. Tighten the bolts firmly.

16 Oil the cam followers and fit them into the holes in which they were originally fitted (marked during dismantling).

17 Check the action of the decompressor on the camshaft gear. Ensure that the spring is undamaged, not stretched, and imparts a positive return action.

18 Check that the toe of the decompressor lever and the two prongs on the weight lever are not worn, and that they remain engaged throughout full travel of the weight lever.

19 Lay the engine on its side and oil the camshaft bearing and insert the camshaft into the crankcase.

20 Mesh the cam gear with the crankshaft gear with the timing marks aligned.

15

18

16

19

17

20

21 Place a new gasket on the crankcase. Oil the camshaft bearing and the crankshaft bearing. Fit the dowel into the crankcase.

22 Fit the ohv oil return pipe into the elongated hole in the crankcase.

23 Fit the crankcase cover, ensuring that the governor slider and washer do not fall off. Guide the internal governor lever into the space between the governor slider and the side of the crankcase. Engage the cover on the dowel and seat the cover onto the crankcase.

24 Secure the crankcase cover with the six bolts. Tighten diagonally opposite bolts a little at a time to avoid distorting or cracking the cover.

25 Insert the valves into the cylinder head. The exhaust valve has the smaller head of the two.

23

21

24

22

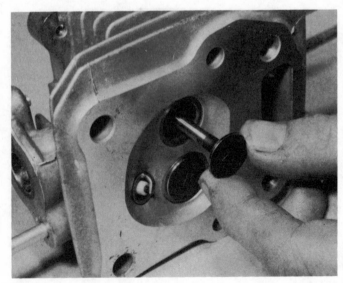

25

26 Place a small block of wood in the cylinder head to hold the valves on the seats while the springs are fitted. Turn the cylinder head on to its face with the wooden block in position.

27 Fit the push rod guide plate onto the two studs in the cylinder head and secure with the two nuts. Place the valve spring over the valve stem.

28 Press the collar down onto the spring, slightly off to one side so that the larger, offset hole in the collar can pass down onto the valve stem, then centralise the collar with a sideways movement so that the smaller hole fits under the shoulder near the tip of the valve stem.

29 Place the two dowels in the top of the cylinder.

30 Place a new gasket on the cylinder.

28

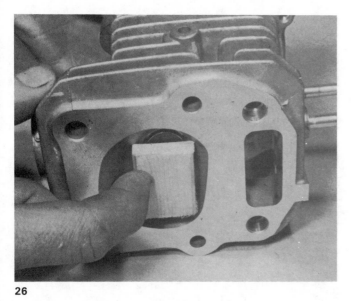

26

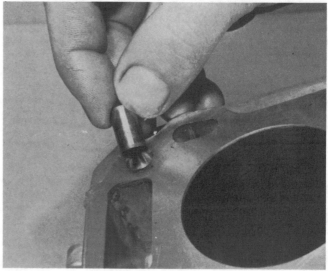

29

27

30

31 Fit the assembled cylinder head onto the cylinder.

32 Secure the cylinder head with the four bolts, tightening them diagonally to avoid distortion or cracking.

33 Insert the push rods through the retainer plate and locate them in the concave holes in the followers.

34 Place the rocker arms onto the studs with the smaller dimple seated on the top of the pushrod.

35 Screw the shouldered nuts onto the studs.

36 Fit the locknuts and set the valve clearances: exhaust 0.005 to 0.007 in (0.13 to 0.18 mm) and inlet 0.003 to 0.005 in (0.08 to 0.13 mm). Lock the locknuts. This operation must be carried out at TDC of the firing stroke.

34

32

35

33

36

37 Fit a new valve cover gasket, then fit the valve cover but do not tighten down as two of the four bolts are used later to install the cowl.

38 Inspect the breather disc valve for damage or distortion. Renew if necessary.

39 Rinse the gauze in solvent, dry thoroughly and insert it into the cavity in the breather housing.

40 Fit a new gasket to the breather cover and secure the cover in position.

41 Place the Woodruff key in the slot in the crankshaft taper. If there are any shear marks or serious burrs, use a new key.

39

37

40

38

41

42 Install the flywheel and the impeller on the crankshaft, aligned with the key. The impeller has four locating pegs which fit into four holes in the flywheel.

43 Fit the rotary screen and starter hub onto the impeller, with the screen located in the hole in the impeller. The three holes in the hub fit onto three pegs on the impeller. Fit the flywheel nut.

44 Install the ignition unit.

45 Using a non-ferrous feeler gauge, set an air gap of 0.010 in (0.25 mm) between the armature legs and the flywheel.

46 Remove the main jet and metering tube and examine them for dirt or gummy deposits. Clean by rinsing and blowing them. **Do not poke the orifices with a needle or wire,** or they may be damaged and the accurate metering lost. Replace the metering tube and the main jet in the carburettor body.

44

42

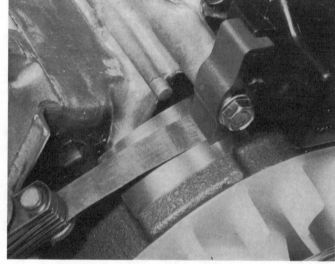

45

43

46

47 To remove the float, pull out the hinge pin. Remove the needle valve by pushing against the coil spring and sliding it out of the slot in the float. Examine the needle head for ridging or wear and renew if necessary.

48 Fit the needle valve back into the slot in the float. Place the float hinge in position between the carburettor hinge posts, with the needle in the hole between the posts. Press the hinge pin through the holes and check it for free movement.

49 Examine the float chamber gasket for distortion or other damage. Renew it if necessary. Ensure that it is properly seated in the groove. Fit the float chamber with the drain plug towards the choke butterfly. Secure it with the bolt and fibre washer.

50 Inspect the four hole seal in the fuel tap and renew it if torn, distorted or hardened. Place it on the two shallow studs.

51 Place the lever valve body in the housing. Fit the wave washer on top of the body.

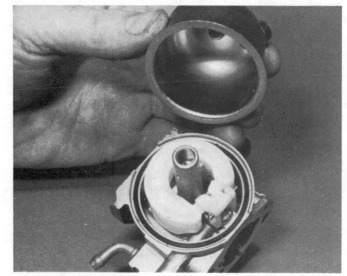

49

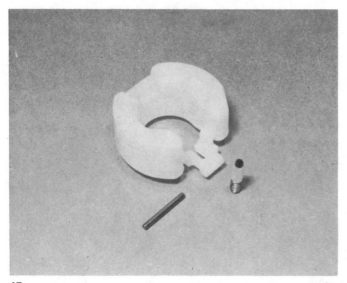

47

50

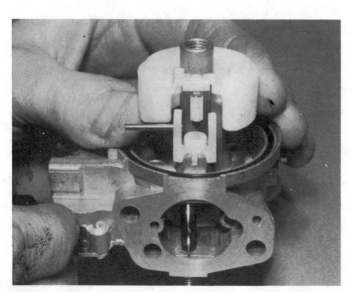

48

51

52 Fit the cover plate onto the housing.

53 Fit a new gasket on the inlet port, place the plastic insulator block on top of it, then fit another new gasket on the insulator block – the small hole in the insulator block must be pointing towards the bottom of the engine.

54 Position the carburettor near the studs and connect the governor link to the larger hole in the throttle butterfly lever. Connect the governor spring to the smaller hole in the lever. Slide the carburettor onto the studs.

55 Fit the gasket, spacer and second gasket to the carburettor intake.

56 Fit the linkage plate to the engine. Connect the short link from the choke butterfly to the lever on the plate. Connect the coil spring from the hole marked STD in the control lever to the small lever at the bottom of the governor lever.

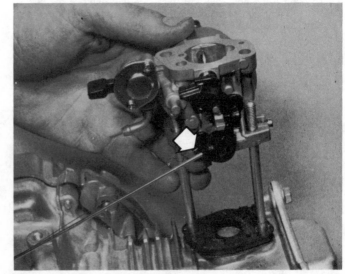

54

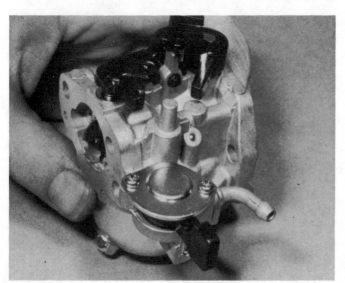

52

55

53

56

57 Fit the guard over the linkage plate.

58 Place the heat shield gasket on the exhaust port studs with the slanted edge positioned as shown in photo 58a ...

... place the muffler on the studs (photo 58b) ...

... and finally, fit the heat shield. Secure with the two nuts (photo 58c).

59 Gently rinse the fuel pipe filter mesh in clean petrol. Blow down the pipe from the other end to remove any particles left on the filter. **Do not** brush or rub it or the mesh will be damaged. Connect the pipe to the tank and secure with the clip.

58b

57

58c

58a

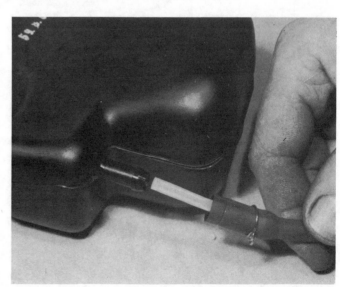

59

60 The fuel tank attaching parts are shown in the photo.

61 Place the washer on the bolt, then the spacer tube. Fit a rubber grip on the tube. Insert the tube and bolt through the hole in the fuel tank, through the other rubber grip and screw the bolt into the mounting bracket on the crankcase.

62 Pass the fuel pipe behind the linkage plate and press the pipe support clip into the hole in the linkage plate. Connect the pipe to the carburettor and secure it with the spring clip. Fit the cowl to the engine with the five bolts.

63 Position the air cleaner duct on the carburettor mounting studs.

64 Secure the air cleaner to the studs with the two nuts. Bolt the air cleaner mounting lug to the linkage plate.

65 Place the spacer on the crankshaft.

66 Fit the Roto-stop ball control plate onto the crankshaft.

67 Connect the two Roto-stop return springs to the two levers and to the anchor bolts.

62

60

63

61

64

65

68 Place the ball retainer on the ball control plate with the balls located in the three concave pressings.

69 Place the brake housing in position with its blisters located on the balls.

70 Place the brake springs on the flange bolts.

71 Line the brake housing up with its three bolt holes in line with the threaded holes in the crankcase cover. Fit the flange bolts and (photo 71a)...

... tighten them down. Fit the Woodruff key into the crankshaft slot (photo 71b).

72 Fit the drive disc onto the crankshaft, aligned with the key.

73 Place the brake lining plate on the drive disc.

66

68

67

69

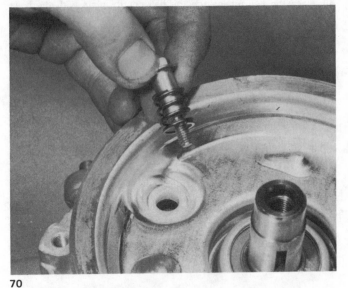

70

72

71a

73

71b

74 Place the clutch spring on the brake lining plate. Fit the driven disc on the brake lining plate with the two pegs in the holes in the brake lining plate. The driven disc has a ball bearing and an oil seal in its centre. Renewal of these is straightforward and the same as for the crankcase bearings described previously.

75 Fit and tighten the central bolt.

76 Examine the seal in the final drive case for damage or distortion. Ensure that it is properly seated in the groove.

77 Renew the oil seal at the bevel drive shaft bearing if necessary. Insert the bevel drive shaft.

78 Place the thrust washer in the casing.

79 Install the bevel gear.

74

77

75

78

76

79

80 Insert the drive selector fork into the bearing in the case.

81 The drive gear shaft and clutch ratchet hub are shown in the photo. The internal coil spring can be renewed by withdrawing the cross key from the slots.

82 Slide the ratchet hub onto the gear shaft splines. Oil the end of the gear shaft and insert it through the bevel gear into the bearing in the case. Engage the hub in the selector fork as the shaft is inserted.

83 Engage the hub ratchet with the bevel gear ratchets.

84 Fit the larger gear flange upwards onto the gear shaft.

82

80

83

81

84

85 Fit the smaller gear onto the shaft (photo 85a) ...

... and then the thrust washer. The cross key in the shaft fits into the cross of the small gear (photo 85b).

86 Insert the drive actuating plunger into the gear shaft.

87 Insert the hollow dowel in the case lip. Fill the case with a light transmission oil.

88 Slide the other half of the case onto the axle, engage it on the dowel and mate the two halves together. Secure with the five bolts. Two are longer and fit one over the extended torque reactor bolt, and the other at the opposite end of the case.

86

85a

87

85b

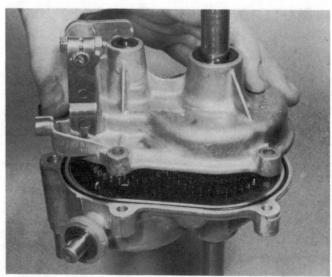

88

89 Clamp the speed selector lever to the selector fork shaft. The index mark on the end of the shaft must coincide with the centre pop mark on the lever.

90 Fit the washer into the hub of the ratchet drive rear wheel.

91 Fit the ratchet freewheel unit into the wheel hub.

92 Place the cover over the hub with the lip pointing outwards.

93 Slide the clamp bracket for the protector plate onto the axle.

91

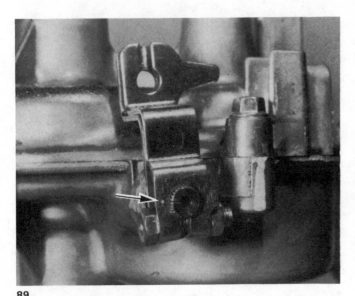

89

92

90

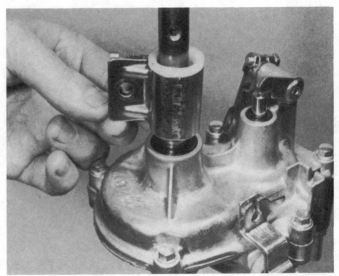

93

94 Bolt the protector plate to the bracket. The tabs on the clamp bracket must be entered in the matching holes in the protector plate.

95 Fit the universal joint onto the drive shaft and secure it by pushing the shear pin through the hole in the shaft.

96 Spring the clip into the groove to retain the pin.

97 Turn the mower frame upside down and lift the axle assembly into position on it. Connect the speed selector cable to the selector fork lever.

98 Connect the drive engage cable to the plunger actuating lever.

96

94

97

95

98

99 Remove the left-hand back wheel to improve access. Fit the shouldered bolt through the curved end plate of the height adjusting lever. Pass the bolt through the height pivoting plate. Fit a washer onto the bolt between the pivoting plate and the boss on the mower frame. Insert the bolt into the higher of the two bosses on the frame and secure it with the nut.

100 Locate the slot in the torque plate on the extended torque reactor bolt on the drive case (photo 100a) ...

... then secure the torque plate with the two bolts (photo 100b).

101 Fit the wheel cup onto the axle with the flange lip inward. Insert the drive pin into the axle hole.

102 Fit the wheel onto the axle so that the drive pin engages the slots in the hub.

100b

99

101

100a

102

103 Secure the wheel with the central bolt and fit the hub cap.

104 To fit the Roto-stop operating cable to the bottom of the engine, connect the nipple in the slot first ...

105 ... then pull the bracket into position and secure it with the two screws. Do not remove the cable sheath retaining spring disc unless a spare is available, as these discs can only be used once. Note that it is not possible to assemble this bracket after the engine has been mounted on the chassis.

106 Mount the engine and secure it with the four bolts.

107 Mount the blade holder on the crankshaft with the blade attachment holes aligned with the holes in the driven disc.

105

103

106

104

107

108 Fit the cutter blade. Hold it with a piece of rag to avoid injury from the cutting edge.

109 Place the spring clip in position next to the groove on the drive shaft. Slide the drive shaft onto the serrations on the drive bevel shaft.

110 Connect the forward universal joint of the drive shaft onto the engine output shaft, align the drive pin hole and insert the pin.

111 Fit the drive shaft guard with the throttle cable located in the slot (photo 111a) ...

... and secure it with the screw (photo 111b).

110

108

111a

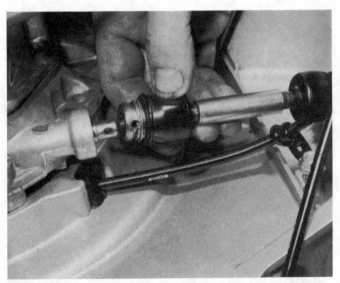

109

111b

112 Connect the throttle cable to the lever on the link plate. Clamp the cable sheath in the clip in a position that gives full range of movement. Push the engine breather pipe onto the air cleaner duct and secure it with the spring clip. Push the other end of the breather pipe into the hole in the crankcase.

113 Adjust the cables as necessary to give correct operation (see Technical Data). The cables in the photo above on the underside of the control quadrant are, from left to right, the Roto-stop, self-propel drive, throttle and speed change.

114 Fit the recoil starter onto the engine cowl.

115 Place the element in the air cleaner housing and fit the cover.

116 Fill the engine with oil to the level shown on the filler plug dipstick.

114

112

115

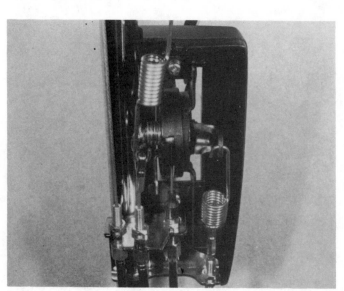

113

116

Recoil Starter Repair

To fit a new recoil spring or starter cord, proceed as follows:-
(1)   Remove the recoil starter from the engine cowl.
(2)   Bend the tang near the cord exit hole up to allow the rope to be unwound.
(3)   Release pulley tension by pulling the cord out about 2 ft, holding the pulley and unwinding the cord. Gently release the pulley.
(4)   Remove the central bolt and lift off the cover. There is no need to lift the pawls or their spring out unless they need renewing, which is straightforward and can be seen in the following views.
(5)   Lift the pulley from the shaft. Remove the recoil spring.

(6)   Hook the outer end of the new spring into the slot in the housing. Wind the spring anti-clockwise into the housing, working in towards the middle. Put a blob of grease in the coils. Attach a new cord to the pulley if necessary and wind it anti-clockwise round the pulley. Place the pulley on the stub shaft and turn it gently anti-clockwise until it engages with the hook on the inner end of the recoil spring.

(7)   If a new cord was fitted, thread the end through the exit hole and knot the handle in place. Inspect the pawls and their spring, renew if damaged. To tension the pulley, wind it about three turns anti-clockwise, hold it and wind the slack in the cord anti-clockwise onto the pulley, then release the pulley.

(8)   Fit the cover with the two legs of the clip on either side of the peg on the pawl (photo 8a) ...

... then fit and tighten the bolt (photo 8b).

(9)   Bend the tang down over the cord. Pull the starter handle and check for freedom of movement and a positive return action. Install the starter on the engine cowl with the handle facing the left side of the mower.

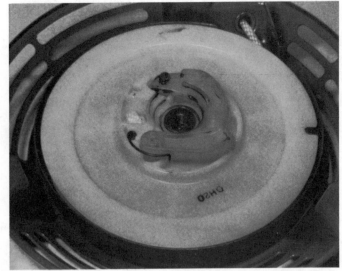

7

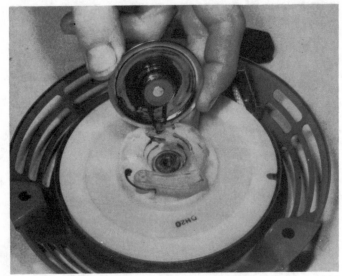

8a

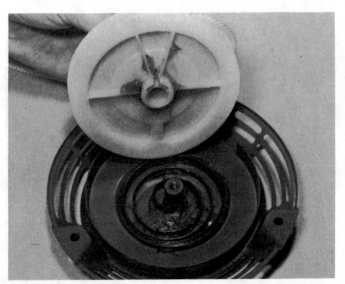

6

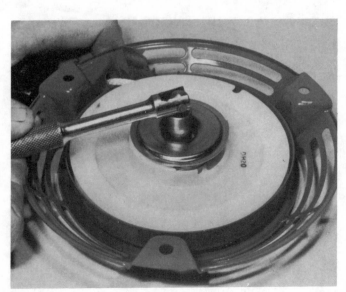

8b

9

Technical Data

Spark plug gap	0.028 to 0.031 in (0.7 to 0.8 mm)
Valve clearances:	
Inlet	0.003 to 0.005 in (0.08 to 0.13 mm)
Exhaust	0.005 to 0.007 in (0.13 to 0.18 mm)
Armature air gap	0.010 in (0.25 mm)
Piston ring gap (standard)	0.009 to 0.020 in (0.23 to 0.525 mm)
Roto-stop brake cable adjustment (free play at tip of lever)	$\frac{3}{16}$ to $\frac{3}{8}$ in (5 to 10 mm)
Drive clutch cable (free play at handle bar)	$\frac{3}{16}$ to $\frac{3}{8}$ in (5 to 10 mm)
Speed change cable (free play at tip of lever)	$\frac{3}{64}$ to $\frac{1}{8}$ in (1 to 3 mm)
Oil	SAE 10W-40

Mountfield M3 power drive

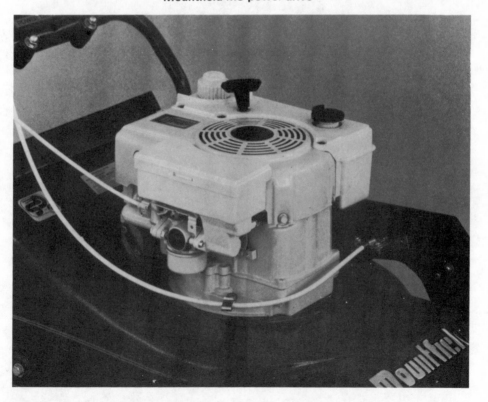

Chapter 9 Mountfield M3 power drive

Introduction

A Tecumseh $3\frac{1}{2}$ hp 4-stroke engine powers the front wheels and the rotary cutter through two separate drives. The mower is fitted with a roller at the rear which is adjusted for cutting height, simultaneously with the two front wheels, by means of a single rotating knob on the frame.

The cutting width is 15 inches and the cutter is not equipped with a drive disconnect or a brake. It therefore rotates whenever the engine is turning. **Do not at any time when the engine is turning, place the hands or any implement under the deck.** Serious injury can result if this vital safety rule is ignored. Never lift the mower to investigate grass blockage or for any other reason when the blades are turning. Always set the engine control to stop and remove the plug lead before touching the cutter or clearing grass blockages.

Grass is ejected at the rear of the casing into a removable grass box. A grass deflector plate hinges down when the grass box is removed to stop particles and hard objects being ejected. Therefore, **do not raise the deflector** while the engine is running. If mowing in severe conditions, the grass box can be removed and the mower used with the deflector plate only. Raising the cutting height reduces the tendency for grass blockage by improving the air flow.

Dismantling

Read Chapter 2 before starting to dismantle. The advice given there will make the approach to dismantling and reassembly better organised and more methodical.

1   Disconnect the plug lead. Drain the oil from the engine.
2   Disconnect the power drive clutch cable from the drive casing.
3   Remove the cutter, the drive sleeve and the key. Remove the exhaust box.
4   Disconnect the throttle cable from the carburettor.
5   Remove the engine mounting bolts. Remove the engine from the deck by unscrewing the bolts in the power drive cover mounting bracket, getting an assistant to pull sideways on the drive cover while the engine is moved sideways to disconnect the power drive. Lift the engine clear when the power drive is disconnected. Remove the plastic dust shield from the power drive shaft.
6   Disconnect the fuel pipe from the tank.
7   Disconnect the air cleaner housing from the carburettor inlet.
8   Remove the engine cowling complete with the air cleaner housing, leaving the fuel tank and recoil starter behind on the engine.
9   Remove the recoil starter from the engine. Remove the fuel tank with the starter handle in it.
10   Note the positions of the governor spring and the link from the governor lever to the throttle butterfly lever, so that they can be reassembled in the same holes. Disconnect the spring and the link and remove the carburettor.
11   Grip the engine drive shaft in a soft jaw vice and remove the flywheel nut. Do not overtighten the vice. If the shaft turns during loosening the flywheel nut, replace the cutter sleeve and key on the drive shaft and grip the sleeve in the vice.
12   Remove the flywheel from the taper (see Chapter 2).
13   Remove the offset key from the drive shaft; remove the plastic sleeve from the shaft.
14   Remove the valve cover.
15   Remove the cylinder head.
16   Remove the crankcase cover, disengaging the power drive pinion as it is withdrawn. Remove the oil pump from the camshaft.
17   Mark the big end cap for reassembly in the same position, then remove it.
18   Withdraw the piston upwards from the cylinder. Ensure that the connecting rod does not score the bore as it passes through.
19   Mark the cam followers for reassembly in the same holes, then remove them.
20   Remove the valves.
21   Remove the breather assembly from the lower part of the crankcase.

Reassembly

1   Fit new oil seals in the crankcase if necessary as described for previous engines.

2   The valve components are shown in the photo in order of assembly.

3   The valve marked with an I in the centre is the inlet valve. **Do not** transpose the valves.

4   Insert the valve into the guide.

5   .Fit the plain hole collar onto the valve stem, dished side to the valve chest. Place the spring against the collar. Fit the slotted collar onto the valve stem, dish into the spring, and offset to allow the valve stem through the wide end of the slot. Lever up the collar and move it sideways so that the narrow end of the slot engages under the shoulder on the valve stem, thus locking the spring onto the valve. Fit both valves in an identical manner (exhaust valve shown here).

3

1

4

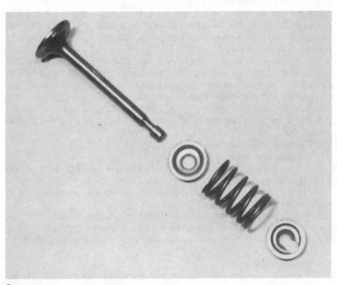

2

5

6 Smear the crankshaft with oil and insert it into the crankcase bearing.

7 Assemble the piston rings and connecting rod on the piston. The rings must be fitted the same way round in the same grooves as when removed. The gudgeon pin and connecting rod must also be the same way round as when removed. Make sure the circlips are located securely. When assembled in the cylinder, the serial numbers on the connecting rod must face the open end of the crankcase.

8 Fit a piston ring clamp to the piston. Oil the cylinder walls. Insert the piston from the top, taking care not to scratch the bore with the connecting rod. Press the piston out of the clamp, tapping gently with a piece of wood if necessary. If an obstruction occurs, do not force the piston in, stop and investigate.

9 Oil the crankpin and engage the big end on it. Fit the cap the correct way round, as marked during dismantling. Tighten the two bolts firmly.

10 Oil the cam followers and insert them in the same holes in which they were originally fitted, as marked during dismantling.

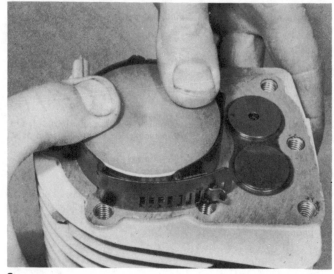

8

6

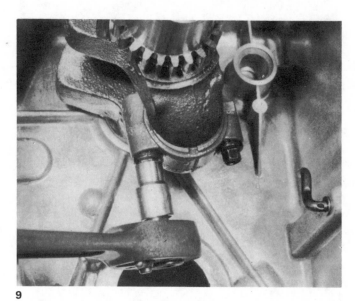

9

7

10

11 Oil the camshaft bearing and insert the camshaft into the crankcase. Mesh the cam gear timing mark in line with the mark on the crankshaft gear.

12 Fit the two dowels into the holes in the crankcase.

13 Fit a new crankcase gasket.

14 Insert the oil pump plunger into the housing ...

15 ... and fit the pump onto the camshaft, with the chamfered side of the hole in the white plastic housing facing down onto the cam gear.

16 The final drive shaft and pinion assembly is held in the crankcase by a circlip with a flat washer behind it.

17 The pinion is keyed to the shaft and has a thrust washer on either side of it, one with an anti-spin angled leg. Removal and installation to fit a new pinion or shaft is straightforward and can be carried out from the photo.

14

11

15

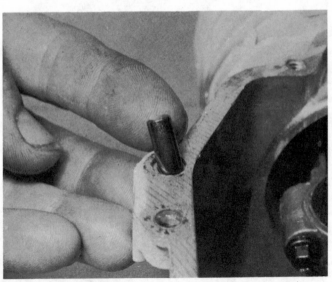

12

16

17

19

18 Check the governor slider and weights for freedom of operation and signs of wear. If faulty, the governor should be renewed as a complete unit. To remove the governor, prise the C-clip out of the groove in the shaft, withdraw the spool, remove the second circlip and lift off the gear assembly and the washer under it. Reassembly is the opposite sequence.

19 The crankcase cover ready for installation is shown in the photo.

20 Oil the crankshaft and the camshaft bearings, then slide the cover onto the crankshaft. Turn the pinion shaft slightly to engage the pinion with the worm on the crankshaft if necessary. Locate the cover on the dowels. Check through the engine breather hole that the oil pump plunger ball-end is correctly in its housing, and that the governor lever is resting correctly against the governor spindle. Fit and tighten diagonally the six bolts and spring washers that secure the housing.

21 Check the valve clearances. Both valves should have a clearance of 0.010 in (0.25 mm). Adjustment of valve clearance is by grinding the tip of the valve stem to increase it or grinding in the valve seat to reduce it, but there are limits to the amount of seat grinding possible. In bad cases, new valves may need fitting. This requires professional attention and the use of special tools.

20

18

21

22 Replace the valve cover with the chamfered corner in the bottom left position.

23 Check the engine breather assembly. The valve in the bottom of the cup must be free, clean and undamaged. Wash the steel wool element in solvent and dry it. Place the circular baffle on the shoulder half way down the cup. Insert the element onto the baffle.

24 Insert the baffle cup assembly into the hole in the crankcase. Fit a new gasket (photo 24a) ...

... then fit the cover and tube and secure with the two bolts and shake-proof washers. Ensure that TOP stamped on the cover is towards the top of the engine (photo 24b).

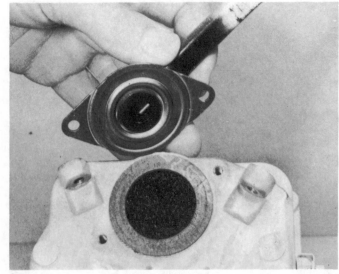

24a

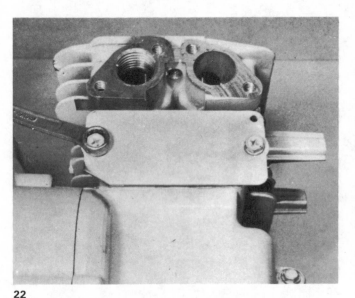

22

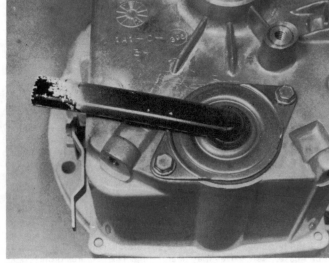

24b

23

25 Fit the plastic sleeve on the crankshaft with its key in the crankshaft groove.

26 Fit the offset key in the slot as shown in the photo, with the longer offset to the left.

27 Fit the flywheel onto the crankshaft, aligned with the key (photo 27a) ...

... and secure with the nut and flat washer (photo 27b).

28 Fit the ignition unit and (photo 28a) ...

... using a non-ferrous feeler gauge set an air gap of 0.015 in (0.37 mm) (photo 28b).

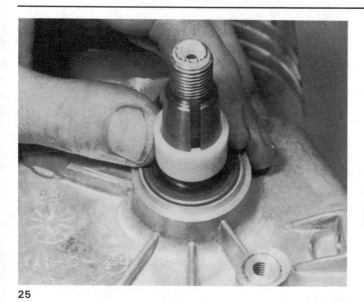

25

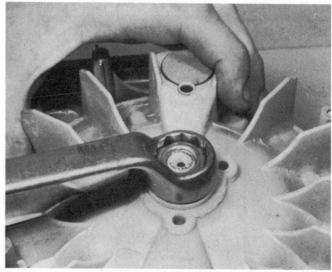

27b

26

28a

27a

28b

29 Fit a new cylinder head gasket and fit the cylinder head, tightening down a little at a time on each bolt in the order shown in the illustration below:

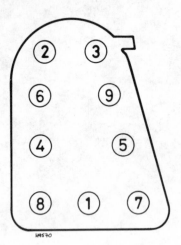

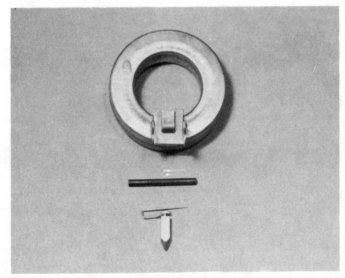

30

30 The float components are shown in the photo. Check the end of the needle valve for ridging or other damage and renew if necessary.

31 Assemble the needle valve on the float with the clip.

32 Position the float hinge between the carburettor hinge lugs, with the needle valve inserted in the fuel entry hole. Insert the hinge pin.

33 Inspect the float bowl seal for damage or distortion and renew if necessary. Fit the bowl onto the carburettor.

34 The bowl is secured with the threaded main jet. Check the main jet for cleanliness and damage. Rinse and blow to clean it. Do not use a pin or wire on the metered holes or they will be damaged and accurate metering lost.

31

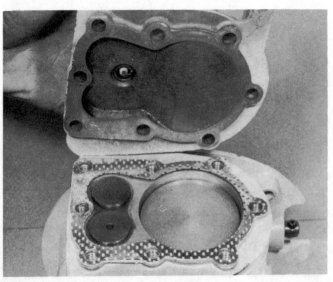

29

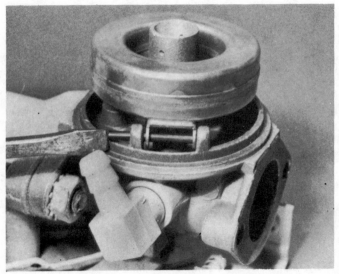

32

33

35

34

36

35 The step on the float bowl must be located as shown in the photo to allow full movement of the float.

36 Fit the carburettor and linkage plate to the engine using a new gasket. Two screws and spring washers are used to secure the carburettor.

37 Connect the link from the throttle butterfly to the hole at the tip of the governor lever. Connect the spring to the next hole in the governor lever, and the link to the lever on the control plate.

37

38 Connect the earth lead to the spade connector on the linkage plate.

39 Connect the fuel pipe to the carburettor. If the recoil starter needs attention, this should be carried out now as it is difficult to deal with the starter cord after the fuel tank and engine cowl have been installed. The main components of the starter are shown in the photo.

40 Drive the central pin out by tapping on the chamfered end, then remove the pulley and recoil spring capsule.

41 Lift the capsule off the pulley.

42 To free the cord, prise out the staple in the pulley. Fit the new cord and tap the staple in again.

43 Fit the new spring capsule onto the pulley and turn it anti-clockwise until the hook on the spring engages in the slot on the pulley hub. This can be verified by increasing tension when turning the capsule.

44 Continue turning the capsule for about four turns to tension the pulley, then use a pin through the hole in the stop lever to engage in the pulley teeth and hold the tension. Wind the cord clockwise onto the pulley when viewed from the capsule side. Leave enough cord free to pass through the hole in the fuel tank and fit the handle.

45 Fit the large clip onto the pulley. Enter the pulley assembly into the housing, ensuring that the legs of the clip are located either side of the divider plate (the tip of the divider plate can just be seen in the photo on the top edge of the housing).

46 Seen from the other side, the photo shows the pulley assembly being entered into the housing with the pin still in the stop lever. Thread the cord under the wire guide.

47 Fit the central pin. Do **not** withdraw the pin from the stop lever yet.

39

42

38

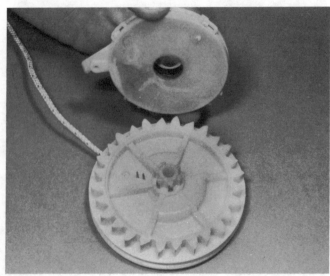

43

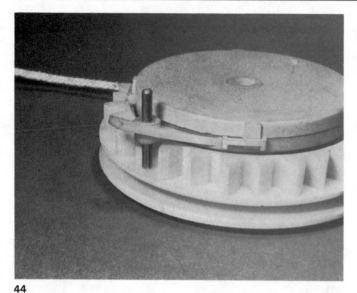

44

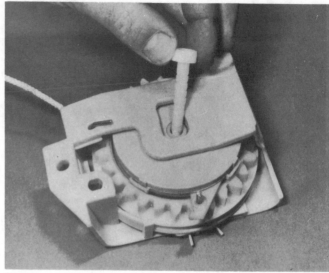

47

45

48 Install the recoil starter on the engine with the two bolts and shake proof washers, fitting the engine fairing plate at the same time, as it is secured by the same screws. Take the pulley tension, withdraw the temporary pin from the stop lever. Pull out some more cord then anchor it temporarily.

49 Fit the engine cowl with the four bolts and shakeproof washers.

50 Fit the oil pipe and secure it to the cowling with the bolt.

51 Thread the cord through the fuel tank hole, slide the fuel tank into the slides on the cowl (photo 51a) ...

... and secure it with the three bolts. Fit the handle to the cord by means of the removable staple. Free the cord from its temporary anchorage. Pull the starter handle to check correct operation and a positive return action (photo 51b).

52 Connect the fuel pipe to the tank and secure it with the spring clip.

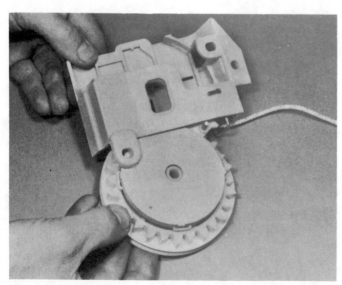

46

48

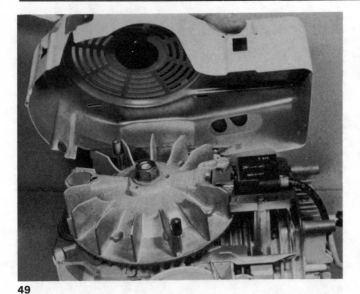

49

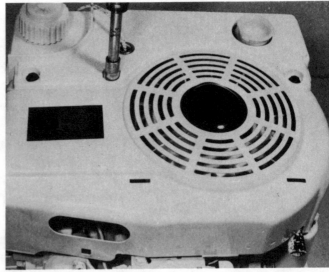

51b

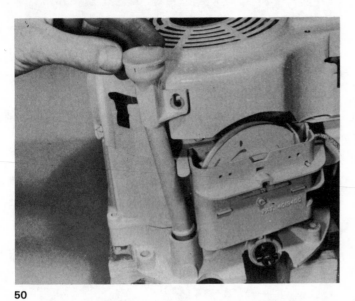

50

53 Insert the air cleaner inlet duct through the hole in the cowling.

54 Check that the rubber ring is in position on the air cleaner housing elbow duct. Connect the engine breather pipe to the tube on the corner of the air cleaner housing. Position the housing elbow on the carburettor inlet flange and secure with the two screws.

55 Wash the air cleaner foam element in solvent and squeeze it dry. Place it in the housing.

56 Fit the press-on lid.

If the power drive unit needs removing, proceed as follows:-
57 Turn the front left-hand wheel backplate until the hole in it exposes the roll pin. Drive the roll pin out and remove the wheel. Withdraw the complete drive unit from the axle.

To re-install the drive unit or fit a new one proceed as follows:-
58 Fit the Woodruff key into the slot in the axle.

51a

53

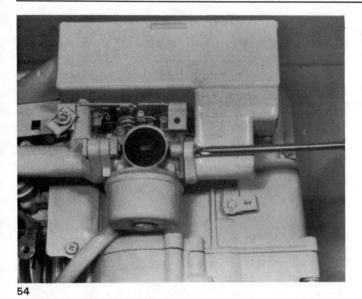

54

58

55

59 The groove in the power drive shaft engages the key on the axle.

60 Place the washer on the plastic bush. Place the bush on the power drive sprocket shaft; push the shaft along the slot until the flats on the plastic bush enter the slot in the drive unit casing. Repeat this operation for the other face of the casing.

61 Slide the housing onto the axle, engaging the groove with the key on the axle.

62 Enter the roll pin into the wheel hub, fit the wheel onto the axle and align the pin with the hole in the axle. Drive the pin into the axle with a hammer and punch, taking care not to damage the pin. Fit the wheel cover plate.

56

59

60

61

62

63 Fit the exhaust manifold to the engine, using a new gasket.

64 Secure the manifold with two bolts and a locking tab.

65 Lower the mower to the minimum cutting height position. Place the engine on the deck. Fit the plastic sleeve on the power drive unit shaft. Enter the engine shaft into the sleeve and engage the drive dogs in the drive unit shaft slots.

66 Bolt the power drive unit to the decking.

67 Fit three of the engine mounting nuts, bolts and flat washers. Connect the exhaust silencer into the manifold pipe and secure it with the fourth engine mounting nut, bolt and flat washers.

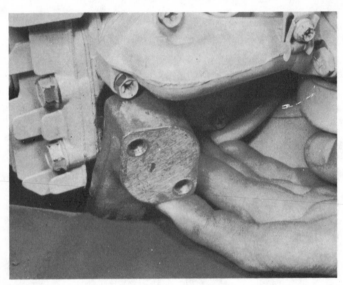

63

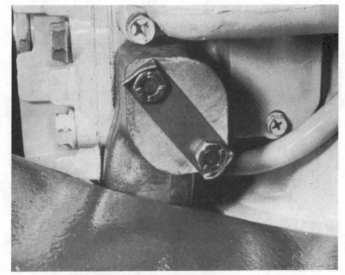

64

65

68 Fit the Woodruff key in the engine drive shaft (photo 68a) ...

... fit the drive sleeve onto the shaft aligned with the key (photo 68b) ...

... and fit the cutter using the shouldered spacer, flat washer and bolt. Use a rag to hold the cutter while tightening it to protect the hand from the cutting edge (photo 68c).

69 Connect the clutch cable to the lever and quandrant.

70 Connect the throttle cable to the lever on the linkage plate.

71 The height adjusting knob attachment fittings are shown in the photo.

72 Screw the knob onto the threaded rod until the shoulder nears the edge of the casting. Place the half collet in the groove. Continue screwing the knob and collet down into the hole in the boss until the hole in the collet aligns with the threaded hole in the boss, then (photo 72a) ...

... screw the grub screw into the boss so that it intercepts the hole in the collet. Tighten the grub screw, and operate the knob to check for free rotation and correct operation of the height adjustment (photo 72b).

66

68a

67

68b

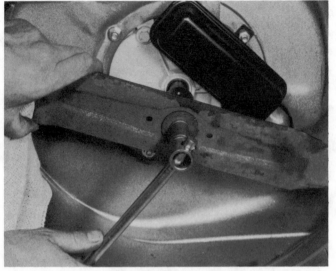

68c

71

69

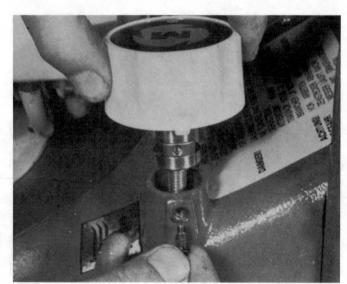

72a

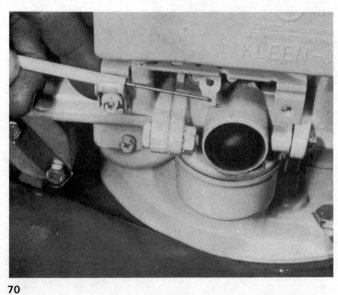

70

72b

Technical data

Spark plug gap	0.030 in (0.8 mm)	Piston ring gap	0.007 to 0.017 in (0.18 to 0.43 mm)
Armature air gap	0.015 in (0.37 mm)	Oil Above 32°F	SAE 30 or SAE 10W30
Valve clearance:		Below 32°F	SAE 5W20 or 5W30 SAE 10W is an acceptable substitute
Inlet and exhaust	0.010 in (0.25 mm)	**Do not use**	SAE 10W40

Webb 14

Chapter 10 Webb 14

Introduction

The Webb 14 is a conventional cylinder mower with a cutting width of 14 inches and is fitted with a Briggs and Stratton 2 hp 4-stroke engine. Two chain drives are taken from the engine, one for the cutting cylinder, the other for the roller which propels the mower along. The drives each have their own clutch, controlled by two hand levers on the handle bar. The roller drive clutch lever is on the right-hand side and is fitted with a trigger enabling it to be locked when pulled to the clutch disengaged position. The left hand lever is pulled to disengage the cutting cylinder drive and has no means of locking in the drive disengaged position. The cylinder clutch acts as a master cylinder and, when disengaged, there is no drive to the rear rollers either.

Adjustment of the cutting height is made by movement of the front rollers after freeing two nuts and bolts on each side plate. A tie bar connects the adjustable plates on either side together to ensure symmetrical adjustment of the rollers from a single adjuster screw on one side plate.

Dismantling

As with the other mowers in this book, read Chapter 2 before starting to dismantle. It contains advice on how to go about dismantling and reassembly in a properly organised manner and will help to make the job easier.

1 Disconnect the plug lead. Drain the oil from the engine.
2 Remove the drive guard and the chain case.
3 Disconnect the throttle cable from the carburettor.
4 Disconnect the ignition cut-off lead from the engine control lever plate.
5 Remove the air cleaner.
6 Remove the two grub screws from the engine to clutch drive plate. Be prepared to take the pressure of the clutch spring as the screws are removed.
7 Remove the engine mounting bolts, slide the engine sideways until the driveshaft is clear of the drive plate hub, then lift the engine clear.
8 Remove the engine cowl.
9 Disconnect the link from the governor vane.
10 Remove the carburettor complete with the fuel tank.
11 Remove the ignition coil and governor vane assembly.

12 Remove the recoil starter clutch housing from the crankshaft threads.
13 Remove the flywheel and the key. To break the flywheel from the taper on the crankshaft, hold the weight of the engine by the flywheel and strike the end of the crankshaft with a soft metal hammer or block. Some assistance will be needed as holding the flywheel is a two-handed job, and the hammer must be used accurately with as little force as possible. **Do not** hit the flywheel impeller blades; they are brittle and will break off.
14 Remove the cylinder head.
15 Remove the valve cover.
16 Remove the crankcase end cover.
17 Turn the crankshaft until there is no load on the cams, then withdraw the camshaft.
18 Mark the cam followers to ensure reassembly into the same holes, then remove them.
19 Remove the oil splasher and big end cap.
20 Mark the piston for reassembly the same way round. Withdraw the piston from the top of the cylinder, making sure that the big end does not scratch the cylinder wall. Mark the gudgeon pin and connecting rod for reassembly, then remove the connecting rod from the piston.
21 Remove the valves.
22 Remove the chain guard and the drive cover.
23 Remove the cutting cylinder double sprocket nut.
24 Remove the rear roller clutch cover.
25 Withdraw the toothed clutch plate and the outer chain.
26 Remove the double sprocket and the inner chain.
27 Remove the top drive sprocket.
28 The bearing for the drive shaft and top sprocket can be removed, after dismantling the clutch assembly, by unscrewing the three nuts and bolts holding the bearing housing to the sideplate. Unless this bearing show signs of wear, or needs cleaning and repacking with grease, or the clutch discs and linings need renewing, there is no need to break down the clutch assembly.
29 If the clutch does need dismantling, pull the clutch and drive shaft from the bearing. Remove the split pin, collar, spring, washer and release hub from the drive shaft. The drive shaft and disc can then be withdrawn from the pilot bearing in the drive plate, complete with the clutch linings.
30 To remove the cutting cylinder and rear roller, undo the nuts, bolts and screws holding the right-hand side plate to the cylinder bearing housing, rear roller bearing housing, cross ties, front roller spindle and bottom blade. Remove the sideplate. Undo the nuts and bolts holding the left-hand side plate to the rear roller and cutting cylinder bearings. Withdraw the roller and cylinder.

Reassembly

1   To fit new crankshaft oil seals, prise out the old ones with a screwdriver. Do not allow the blade to score the side of the seal housing or an oil seepage may result. Oil each new seal and tap it gently into the crankcase hole. The sharp line of the seal must face in towards the crankcase interior.

2   Oil the crankshaft and insert it into the crankcase.

3   Fit the connecting rod to the piston, insert the gudgeon pin and secure with a circlip. The connecting rod and gudgeon pin must be assembled the same way round as they were originally installed.

4   Note the small step on the big end of the connecting rod. This mates with a nib on the big end cap to ensure that the cap is fitted the right way round.

5   Fit a piston ring clamp to the piston, oil the cylinder bore, then pass the connecting rod down through the bore and the piston into the top. Take care that the bore is not scratched by the connecting rod as the latter passes through. Press the piston into the bore, sliding it out of the clamp. Tap it gently with a piece of wood if necessary, but if obstructed, stop and investigate or the rings may be broken.

6   Oil the crankpin and engage the big end on it. Fit the big end cap with the nibs in the connecting rod recesses, fit the oil splasher and secure with the two cap bolts. Tighten the bolts firmly; if they come loose the results will be severe damage and probably a wrecked engine. Turn the crankshaft to ensure freedom of movement.

7   Fit the cam followers into the same holes out of which they came.

8   Oil the camshaft bearings, and fit the camshaft. The timing mark on the cam gear must be aligned with the index mark on the crankshaft gear when the two gears are meshed.

9   Fit a new gasket to the crankcase cover of the same thickness as the original one. Oil the crankshaft and the camshaft. Fit the cover onto the crankcase dowels and tap gently all round with a piece of wood to seat the cover.

10 Fit the six bolts and spring washers. Tighten them a little at a time diagonally to avoid distorting or cracking the cover.

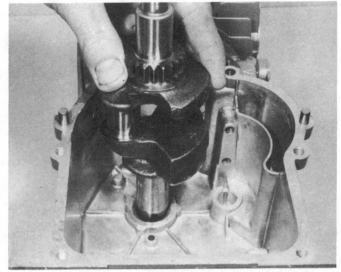

2

3

1   4

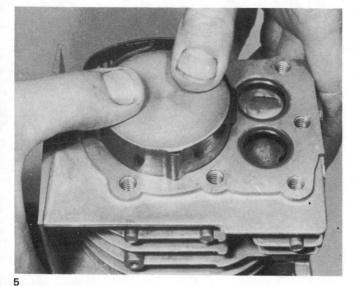

5

8

6

9

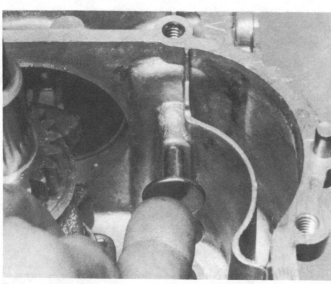

7

10

11 The valve components are shown in the photo. The elongated hole in the collar allows the valve stem shoulder to pass through the collar. The collar is then moved sideways to engage the small end of the hole in the centre of the collar under the shoulder of the valve stem. A notch in the rim of the collar shows which way to push the collar to engage the shoulder and thus lock the valve spring in position.

12 Fit the valves. The exhaust valve has the smaller head of the two. The crankshaft should be turned to TDC of the firing stroke, to ensure that the cam followers are at their lowest position in the valve chest, before placing the collar and valve spring in the valve chest. The collar notch must be facing outwards.

13 Insert the valve until it seats, lever the collar up over the valve stem until the shoulder on the stem can be seen, then push the collar sideways to engage it on the shoulder.

14 Check the valve clearances, with the engine still at TDC of the firing stroke. The inlet valve clearance is 0.005 to 0.007 in (0.13 to 0.18 mm). The exhaust valve clearance is 0.009 to 0.011 in (0.23 to 0.28 mm). If the clearance is too great, the valve must be ground in; if too small, the end of the valve stem must be ground off.

15 Fit a new cylinder head gasket and fit the cylinder head.

13

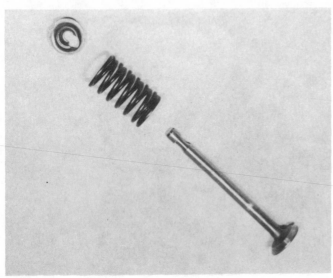

11

14

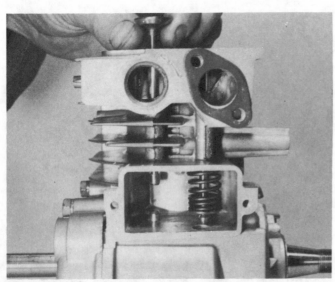

12

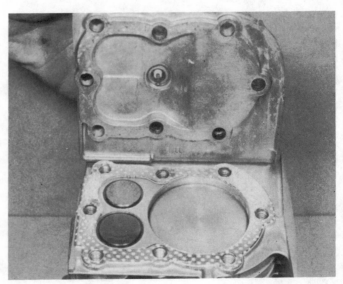

15

16 Place the cylinder shroud in position, fit the seven cylinder head bolts and tighten them a little at a time in a diagonal order to avoid distorting or cracking the cylinder head.

17 Check that the disc valve in the breather is not stuck or binding. A wire gauge or feeler 0.045 in (1.1 mm) in thickness should not enter the gap between the fibre disc and the body. Do not use force when making this check or the internal bracket holding the disc in place may be distorted. Fit a new gasket to the breather cover (photo 17a) ...

... fit it in position and secure it with the two screws and spring washers (photo 17b).

18 Inspect the flywheel key for shear marks; if present fit a new key. Note that the key is made of zinc, designed to shear if shock loaded without damaging the crankshaft or engine. **Do not** fit a hard metal key.

19 Install the flywheel on the crankshaft with the slot aligned with the key.

17b

16

18

17a

19

20 Place the washer on the flywheel.

21 Screw the recoil starter housing onto the crankshaft threads and tighten. If the ratchet or internal drive balls need attention, the retainer cover complete with the ratchet can be removed by prising the cover off the housing with a wedge or a screwdriver. Clean the ratchet by wiping with cloth only.

22 Fit the ignition coil unit and governor vane onto the crankcase mountings and secure it with the two bolts and flat washers, but do not tighten at this stage. Using a non-ferrous feeler gauge set the air gap between the armature and the flywheel to 0.006 to 0.010 in (0.15 to 0.25 mm). Tighten the two bolts.

23 Remove the needle valve and inspect the needle for damage and dirt. Remove the needle holder and examine the metering hole recessed into the carburettor body; if it is dirty or gummy, unscrew and withdraw it for cleaning. **Do not** use a pin to clean the orifice as this will cause damage and spoil the metering. Rinse the hole out with clean petrol and blow it clear. Screw the metering body back into the carburettor body, and tighten it with care so that the slot is not burred. Unscrew the needle valve well back in the body, check that the washer on the body is in good condition, then screw the body into the carburettor and tighten. Gently screw the needle valve right in, then unscrew it $1\frac{1}{2}$ turns. This will give a setting that allows the engine to be started later for warm-up and fine tuning.

24 Examine the filter on the end of the fuel pipe for damage and cleanliness. **Do not** rub this mesh to clean it as it is very fragile. Unscrew the pipe from the carburettor and rinse it in clean petrol, then blow the screen to remove any particles. A check valve is contained inside the tube. Blow down the carburettor end of the pipe and ensure that this valve seats and stops the flow of air. Suck and ensure that air flow is unobstructed. Screw the pipe back into the carburettor.

25 If the gasket between the carburettor and fuel tank is damaged, fit a new one. Fit the carburettor to the fuel tank with the two bolts and washers.

26 Screw the exhaust silencer into the exhaust port and lock it with the locking ring, in a position with the box offset away from the carburettor.

27 Connect the governor link to the throttle butterfly lever (photo 27b) then install the carburettor using a new gasket. It is easier to engage the governor link while the carburettor is still free.

28 Connect the ignition cut-out lead to the connector on the engine control lever plate.

21

22

20

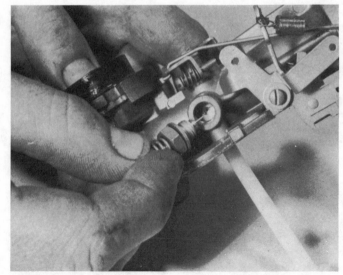

23

24

27a

25

27b

26

28

29 Attach the rotary screen to the flywheel with the two bolts.

30 Install the engine cowling and secure it with three bolts and one of the cylinder head bolts. If the recoil starter needs attention, carry out the procedure in Recoil Starter Repair later in this chapter before installing the cowling.

31 Fit the square side cowl and secure it with one nut and washer.

32 To clean the air cleaner foam element, wash it in solvent and squeeze it dry (do not wring it out). When dry, oil it lightly and install it in the housing.

33 Fit the cover to the housing.

34 Fit the cutting cylinder bearing holder onto the spindle at the right-hand end of the cylinder.

35 Secure the bearing by threading the screw into the spindle and tightening.

36 Fit the bearing housing onto the left-hand end of the cutting cylinder. Place the collar on the spindle. Insert the spindle into the left side plate of the chassis, complete with cutter and bearing assembly. Secure the bearing housing to the side plate with the nut and bolt, but do not tighten.

37 Tilt the lever on the bearing housing upward. Pass the cutting cylinder adjustment screw through the bracket on the end of the bearing housing lever. Fit the spring in the protective sleeve onto the screw, then thread the screw into the pivot block on the side plate.

38 Fit the triangular bearing housing at each end of the rear roller spindle. The bearing at the right-hand end is secured by the bolt threaded into the spindle. The left-hand end has a collar on the spindle similar to the cutting cylinder and is inserted through the side plate like the cylinder. Secure the bearing housing to the side plate with the three nuts and bolts.

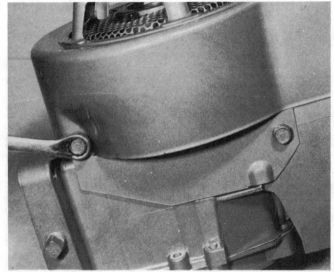

30

31

29

32

33

36

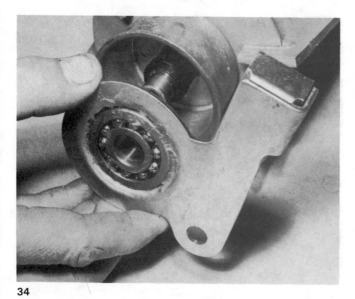

34

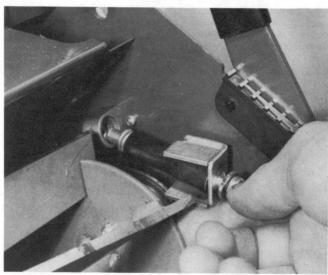

37

35

38

39 The line-up at the right-hand side of the chassis prior to fitting the side plate is shown in the photo.

40 Fit the side plate onto the cross ties and secure with the self-locking nuts and washers. Secure the bottom blade with the two set screws. Position the triangular plate over the rear roller bearing housing holes and secure the bearing housing to the side plate and triangular plate with the three nuts and bolts. Tilt the cutting cylinder bearing housing to line it up with the hole in the side plate and loosely fit the nut and bolt. Fit the adjuster screw and spring in the same way as described previously for the left-hand side plate.

41 Fit the large sprocket to the rear roller axle. Fit the clutch plate and sprocket (the sprocket is out of sight behind the clutch plate in the photo).

42 Place the chain on the clutch plate sprocket and the rear roller sprocket. Connect the chain with the removable link and spring clip shown in the photo. The closed end of the clip must be pointing in the direction of chain travel. The remaining drive chains and sprockets are assembled after the main drive clutch assembly has been installed as follows.

43 Check the pilot bearing for wear, renew if necessary. Apply a small quantity of grease, but not too much or it may contaminate the clutch.

44 Fit the drive shaft into the pilot bearing. If the drive shaft disc is worn, it can be separated from the shaft by undoing the socket grub screw in the hexagon and withdrawing the shaft from the hexagon. A new disc and hexagon can then be fitted to the drive shaft.

45 Place a clutch lining onto the drive shaft disc.

46 Place the clutch pressure plate on the lining.

47 Place the second lining on the pressure plate.

48 Place the release hub on the drive shaft.

40

41

39

42

43

46

44

47

45

48

49 Fit the washer, spring and collar onto the drive shaft.

50 Press the collar down with a hollow tube, line up the hole in the collar with the hole in the shaft and insert the split pin.

51 Fit the oil seal onto the shaft.

52 Insert the drive shaft into the bearing, engaging the release hub with the rollers on the release fork at the same time.

53 Check the key for shear marks or other damage and renew if necessary. Place the key in the drive shaft groove (photo 53a) ...

... then fit the sprocket (photo 53b) ...

... and secure it with the self-locking nut (photo 53c).

54 Fit the lower sprocket and chain.

55 Fit and adjust the chain tensioner to give about half an inch of sideways slack in the chain.

51

49

52

50

53a

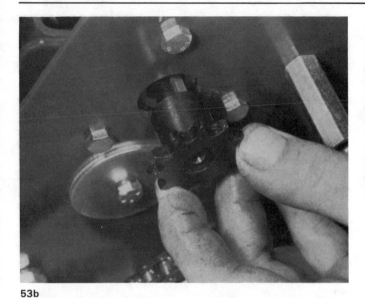

53b

55

53c

56 The ball race in the clutch lining sprocket fits onto the clutch plate (shown in the photo before the clutch plate was assembled onto the shaft). Inspect the cork inserts for wear. If renewal is necessary, all corks must be replaced as a set, otherwise uneven action and slipping will occur.

57 Fit the clutch lining sprocket and chain.

58 Fit and tighten the double sprocket self-locking nut.

59 Fit and adjust the chain tensioner to give about half an inch of sideways slack in the chain.

60 Insert the clutch release plunger into the hollow shaft.

61 Slide the clutch cover onto the three pillars.

62 Fit the clutch springs, washers and screws. Tighten each screw **exactly** the same number of turns, sufficiently to give a positive drive with no clutch slip. Setting is a trial and error procedure after completing assembly, but do not overtighten or the spring coils may be damaged when the clutch is disengaged; clutch operation will also be heavy.

54

56

57

58

59

60

61

62

63 Adjust the socket screw against the release plunger, then back off sufficiently to ensure a little free play in the lever. Tighten the adjuster locknut.

64 The photo shows the chain drives correctly assembled before the chain guard is fitted.

65 Secure the chain guard in position on the side plate.

66 Connect the cable from the right-hand handle bar lever to the main drive clutch release fork. The cable must be located in the slotted lug in the engine side guard, visible in the view shown previously in photograph 40.

67 Connect the cable from the left-hand handle bar to the rear roller drive clutch. The lever can be seen in the photo with the coil return spring attached to it.

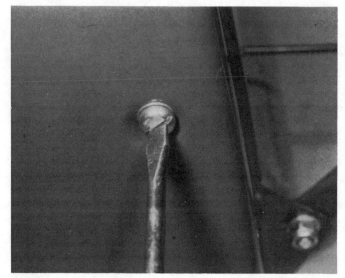

65

63

66

64

67

68 Lift the engine onto the chassis. Slide it so that the drive shaft passes through the hole in the guard plate. Fit the key in the drive shaft groove and slide the shaft into the clutch drive plate.

69 Fit the engine mounting bolts.

70 Screw the two grub screws into the hub of the clutch drive plate and tighten.

71 Fit the drive guard.

72 Connect the throttle cable to the engine control lever.

73 Clamp the cable sheath in a position that ensures full range of movement of the engine control lever. The sheath will be marked where it was originally clamped and this should indicate the required position. A new cable obviously needs some trial and error to select the correct position.

70

68

71

69

72

73

8

Recoil Starter Repair

If the starter needs renewing or the recoil spring breaks, proceed as follows.

(1)   Remove the cowling from the engine.

(2)   Bend the tags up from the pulley housing. Free pulley tension if necessary by turning the pulley anti-clockwise sufficiently to obtain some slack cord, then unwind the cord from the pulley. Release the pulley gently, then carefully lift it out of the housing. Remove the handle from the cord if fitting a new cord.

(3)   A new cord can then be fitted by passing the end through the hole in the pulley and knotting it. Wind the cord anti-clockwise onto the pulley.

(4)   To fit a new tensator spring, free the end of the old spring from the slot in the cowling. Remove the old spring. Hook the outer end of the new spring into the slot and coil the spring anti-clockwise into the housing.

(5)   Fit the pulley into the housing, turning it gently anti-clockwise to pick up the hook at the inner end of the spring. Feed the cord through the hole in the housing.

(6)   Fit the handle onto the cord and knot the cord as described in Chapter 2.

(7)   Tension the pulley by turning it anti-clockwise about 3 turns. Wind the spare loops of cord onto the pulley in a clockwise direction; it may be necessary to ease the pulley out slightly to create a gap for the cord to be wound. Gently release the pulley. Bend the two opposing tags down to retain the pulley in the housing.

(8)   Fit the cowling onto the engine, engaging the ratchet shaft correctly into the pulley hole.

(9)   Pull the starter handle and check for proper engagement of the drive, free movement and a positive return action.

Technical Data

Spark plug gap	0.030 in (0.7 mm)
Armature air gap	0.006 to 0.010 in (0.15 to 0.25 mm)
Valve clearance:	
Inlet	0.005 to 0.007 in (0.13 to 0.18 mm)
Exhaust	0.009 to 0.011 in (0.23 to 0.28 mm)
Breather disc valve clearance	0.045 in (1.1 mm) wire gauge must not enter space between valve and body
Crankshaft end float	0.002 to 0.008 in (0.05 to 0.20 mm)
Piston ring gap (wear limit):	
compression rings	0.035 in (0.80 mm)
oil ring	0.045 in (1.14 mm)
Oil	
40°F to 100°F	SAE 30, 10W-30 10W-40
0°F to 60°F	SAE 10W-30, 10W-40
Below 0°F	SAE 5W-20, 5W-30

2

Atco Commodore 14

Chapter 11 Atco Commodore 14

Introduction

Four different cutting widths are available in the Commodore range of cylinder mowers: 12, 14, 17 and 20 inch. All are powered by the Atco 114 cc 4-stroke engine and all have the same features. The mower dealt with in this chapter is the B14 14 inch model.

A 'deadman's handle' type full-width lever on the handle bar must be pulled up to the handle bar to engage the drive for both the cutting cylinder and the rear roller self-propelled drive. A smaller lever on the right-hand side of the handle bar can be pulled independently to engage the cutting cylinder drive only. The smaller lever is overlapped by the full-width lever so that it is operated automatically when the full-width lever is pulled. If the hands are removed from the handle bar, the levers return automatically to the disengaged position, thus stopping mower travel and the cutting cylinder.

Cutting height is adjusted by a micro-adjuster knob on the left side of the frame, without the need to use other tools to unlock or operate the adjustment. The adjustment raises or lowers the front rollers. To cut long grass the front rollers can be removed and two side wheels fitted. The rollers are suitable for all normal length lawn cutting and allow the mower to overlap the edge of the lawn, thus cutting right to the edge.

12

Dismantling

Read the hints and tips on overhauling in Chapter 2 before starting to dismantle. An orderly and methodical approach to dismantling and reassembly will make the overhaul task much easier. To dismantle the mower proceed as follows.
1   Disconnect the plug lead. Drain the oil from the engine.
2   Remove the clutch cover (this is the guard which has the Commodore B14 motif on it).
3   Remove the engine outer cowl, complete with the recoil starter.
4   Remove the starter handle from the side of the handle bar and lift the outer cowl and recoil starter clear.
5   Remove the throttle cable support bracket from the top of the carburettor and disconnect the cable from the throttle connector. Leave the cable sheath attached to the support bracket to keep the adjustment.
6   Remove the engine, sliding it sideways to disengage the coupling half-housing and rubber coupling. Lift the engine mounting from the platform. Remove the inner cowl.
7   Remove the carburettor.
8   Remove the silencer.
9   Remove the engine cowl.
10 Remove the starter drive hub from the flywheel.
11 Remove the left-hand threaded flywheel nut.

12 Rig up a flat extractor plate as shown above and use $\frac{1}{4}$ UNC bolts in the flywheel puller holes to remove the flywheel from the crankshaft.
13 Remove the cylinder head.
14 Remove the crankcase cover.
15 Check that the crankshaft gear and camshaft gear have timing marks that coincide with each other at Top Dead Centre of the firing stroke. **The cam gear on the example used was not marked.** Make suitable marks if necessary.
16 With the engine at TDC of the firing stroke, remove the camshaft.
17 Mark the cam followers for reassembly in the same holes and remove them.
18 Remove the big end cap and oil splasher.
19 Remove the carbon step from the top of the cylinder with a soft tool, then withdraw the piston and connecting rod from the top of the cylinder. Do not allow the big end to scratch the cylinder bore.
20 Remove the breather assembly from the valve chest.
21 Remove the valves.
22 Remove the air cleaner housing from the carburettor. Take out the thin gauze, foam element and thick gauze from the housing.
23 Remove the float chamber from the carburettor and dismantle the float, needle valve and main jet emulsion tube assembly.

24 Remove the chain cover from the left-hand side.
25 Remove the chains by removing their split links (i.e. one link on each chain has a spring clip holding it on. Find and remove this clip then remove the link).
26 Remove the three screws from the rear roller drive clutch drive plate, together with the clutch spring on each screw, then remove the drive plate.
27 Carefully pull the chain wheel and cork assembly off the clutch boss, taking care not to lose any of the ball bearings around the central hole.
28 Jam the cutting cylinder and unscrew the double sprocket anti-clockwise.
29 Remove the clutch operating push rod from the central spindle. The push rod is in two parts, one short, one long, separated from each other by a thrust ball.
30 The removal of the rear roller sprocket, top drive sprocket and the side frame is self-evident and should not present any difficulties.

31 Remove and dismantle the main clutch. This is straightforward and is the reverse of the assembly process described later.

3

Reassembly

1   The crankshaft oil seals can be renewed if necessary in the same way as described for other engines in earlier chapters.

2   Inspect the condition of the governor teeth and check that the spool moves freely up and down. Renew the assembly if necessary. It can be detached from the shaft by removing the C-clip from the shaft, lifting the spool off, removing the bottom C-clip and lifting the toothed carrier and weights assembly.

3   Oil the crankshaft bearing surface and insert it into the crankcase.

4   The method of assembling the big end cap and oil splasher on the connecting rod is shown in the photo. Note the nibs on the cap and the connecting rod. These must be adjacent. If the connecting rod has been removed from the piston, reassemble it the same way round as when it was removed, and insert the gudgeon pin the same way round as when removed.

4

5   Fit a piston clamp to the piston. Oil the bore, especially at the top. Insert the piston from the top of the cylinder, taking care that the big end of the connecting rod does not scratch the bore. Press the piston out of the clamp and into the cylinder. Tap it gently with a piece of wood if necessary, but do not force it if there is an obstruction. Start again, applying more oil to the bore. The lettering on the connecting rod web must be facing towards the still open end of the crankcase after assembly.

2

5

6   Engage the big end on the crankshaft. Fit the big end cap and the oil splasher. Tighten the big end bolts firmly. The oil splasher must point to the base of the crankcase.

7   Invert the engine and insert the cam followers. Each should be fitted into the same hole from which it was removed to ensure that wear patterns are compatible.

8   Oil the camshaft bearing. Insert the camshaft into the crankcase. Mesh the cam gear and crankshaft gear with the timing marks aligned.

9   Lay the engine flat and fit a new gasket to the crankcase, of the same thickness as the old one.

10   Oil the crankshaft and camshaft bearing surfaces. Fit the cover onto the crankcase, ensuring that it locates properly on the dowels.

8

6

9

7

10

11 Fit the bolts, tightening them a little at a time diagonally to avoid distorting or cracking the cover.

12 The method of assembly of the valve components is shown in the photo.

13 Place the valve spring in position in the valve chest, with the collar under it and the dish on the collar facing up into the spring. Insert the valve into the guide. Note that the exhaust valve has an X marked on the head; it must therefore be fitted opposite the exhaust port (see photo 13b).

14 Prise up the collar with a pair of long nose pliers and insert the pin through the hole in the valve stem.

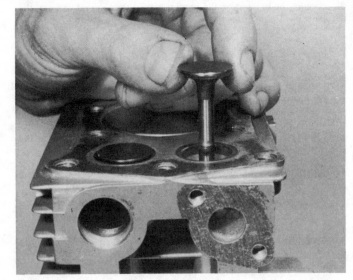

13a

11

13b

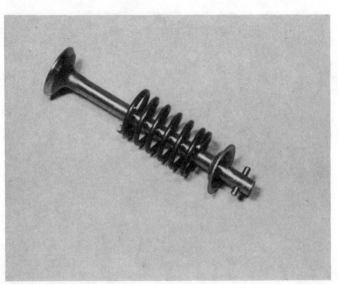

12

14

15 Check that the breather disc valve is not distorted and that it is not binding or stuck. Fit a new gasket to the breather assembly.

16 Fit the breather with the strainer to the right.

17 Place a new cylinder head gasket on the cylinder and fit the cylinder head.

18 Tighten the bolts a little at a time in diagonal rotation. Two of them will have to be removed later to fit the cowl on the engine.

19 Install the ignition assembly with the high tension lead through the hole in the casting and the low tension lead through the conduit which is positioned in the other hole in the casting. Although the ignition mounting plate has slots at both the fixing screws, in practice it picks up the screw holes in one position only.

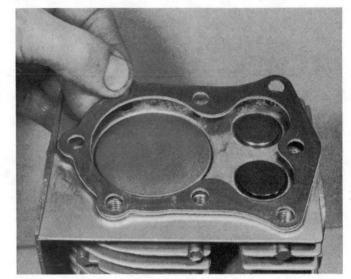

17

15

18

16

19

20 Check that the Woodruff key is free from shear marks and other damage; renew it if necessary. Place it in the slot in the crankshaft.

21 Place the flywheel on the crankshaft, aligning it carefully with the key. Do not attempt to screw the flywheel nut on and tighten it unless the key is properly engaged.

22 Fit the flat washer and flywheel nut and tighten.

23 Fit the front cover plate with the high tension lead located in the blister. Screw the plug cap into the end of the lead.

24 Fit the starter drive hub with the two screws and washers.

25 Check that the emulsion tube and main jet assembly is clean and free from gummy deposits. Screw it into the carburettor body. Examine the gasket, it must be properly seated and free from damage and distortion.

22

20

23

21

24

25

27

26 Check the pointed end of the float needle valve for ridging or other damage; renew it if necessary. Fit the shoulder of the needle into the fork on the float. Lower the needle into the hole in the carburettor body complete with the float.

27 Align the float hinge with the holes in the carburettor hinge lugs and fit the float pin.

28 Fit the float chamber. The flat step must be on the same side as the float hinge to allow full float movement, with the tickler push button nearest the carburettor air filter housing. If the tickler leaks or the rod is damaged it can be removed (before fitting the float chamber) by holding the rod against its internal seat gasket, pushing the button against the spring, then moving it sideways until the slot clears the rod end. Assembly of new parts is carried out in the reverse order.

29 Fit the large mesh screen into the air filter housing (photo 29a) ...

... then the foam element (if not new, wash in solvent and thoroughly dry) (photo 29b) ...

... and finally the small mesh screen (photo 29c).

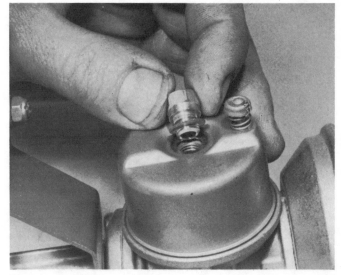

28

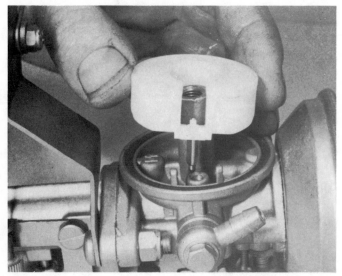

26

29a

29b

30

29c

31

30 Fit the air cleaner cover and secure with the central screw and flat washer. The inlet of the cover must be facing downward when the carburettor is on the engine.

31 Place a new gasket in position on the inlet port.

32 Fit the carburettor onto the inlet port.

33 Screw the exhaust connecting pipe with the washer gasket on it into the exhaust port.

34 Secure the silencer with the nut and flat washer. The throttle return hair spring can be seen at the bottom of photo 34a. Its lower end is connected into ...

... the throttle lever and the throttle cable connector hanging from it (photo 34b).

Connect the low tension lead to the spade connection.

35 Place the Woodruff key in the crankshaft slot. Fit the half-coupling onto the crankshaft, aligned with the key. Secure it temporarily with the two set screws. Some repositioning of the half-coupling may be necessary when the engine is installed.

32

33

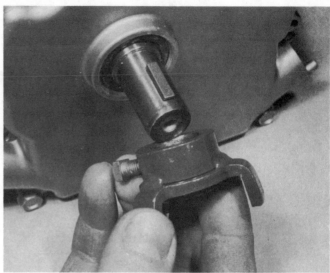

35

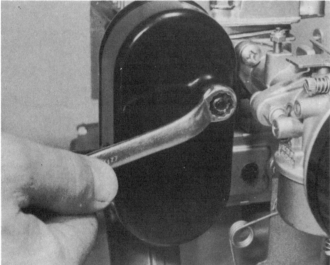

34a

36 Press the rubber coupling into the half-coupling.

37 The main drive clutch release mechanism components are shown in the photo in their correct order of assembly.

38 Fit the cable through the bracket. Place the spring cup over the cable and locate it on the end of the sheath adjuster. Pass the cable through the spring and the other spring cup, then through the hole in the bottom of the release fork. Slide the nipple retainer slot onto the cable to retain the assembly against spring pressure.

39 Slide the collar and the spring onto the driven shaft. Fit the Woodruff key into the slot in the shaft.

40 The groove in the bore of the release hub engages with the key in the driven shaft.

41 Slide the clutch release assembly onto the driven shaft.

42 Press the assembly against the spring and secure it with the set bolt and washer.

34b

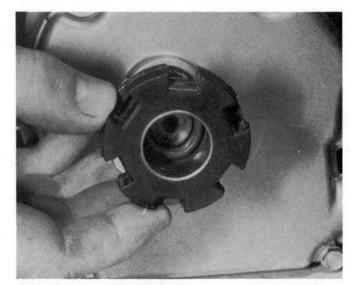

36

37

40

38

41

39

42

43 Bolt the cable bracket to the platform. Thread the rear roller drive clutch cable (the upper cable in the photo) through the release lever (partly hidden behind the driven shaft in this view).

44 Fit the plastic ferrule onto the cable nipple and press the ferrule into the hole in the side frame.

45 Fit the square drive sleeve onto the driven shaft.

46 Place a clutch lining onto the driven shaft (photo 46a) ...

... then a disc onto the square sleeve (photo 46b) ...

... then the second clutch lining (photo 46c) ...

... and finally the second disc (photo 46d).

47 Align the hole in the square sleeve with the hole in the shaft and insert the split pin. Bend the legs of the split pin to secure it in the hole.

45

43

46a

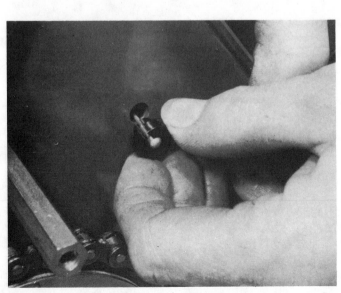

44

46b

46c

46d

47

48 Fit the clutch housing onto the driven shaft, engaging the square slots with the projections on the clutch linings.

49 Secure the clutch housing on the shaft with the screw, large flat washer and small washer.

50 Place the engine mounting on the platform with the clutch cables underneath it and located in their respective slots in the mounting.

51 Lift the engine onto the mounting and engage the rubber coupling in the clutch cover coupling.

52 Fit the engine mounting bolts.

53 It may be necessary to loosen the coupling set screws and slide the half-coupling along the shaft to align the engine over the mounting holes, and also to achieve shaft alignment and full engagement of the coupling. Tighten the set screws when the correct position has been set.

54 Screw the main drive sprocket onto the shaft.

55 Screw the double sprocket onto the cutting cylinder axle. Fit the clutch boss.

48

49

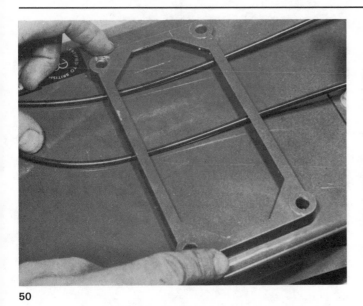

50

53

51

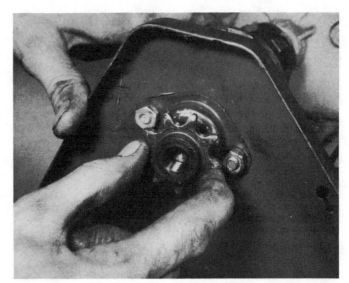

54

52

55

56 Insert the clutch operating push rod.

57 Smear grease in the groove of the chain wheel with the clutch corks, and place the ball bearings in the groove.

58 Fit the chain wheel onto the clutch boss, keeping it square to avoid displacing the balls.

59 Fit the drive plate onto the three posts on the clutch base. Place a clutch spring on each post then secure them with the three screws.

60 Fit the drive chains. All spring links must be fitted with the rounded end facing in the direction of chain travel.

61 Set the chain tensioner (the vertical arm with the oval snubber on it) to give about $\frac{1}{2}$ inch of slack in the chain length not in contact with the snubber. Fit the chain guard cover.

62 Hook the governor spring into the loop in the vertical link shown by the arrow in the photo.

58

56

59

57

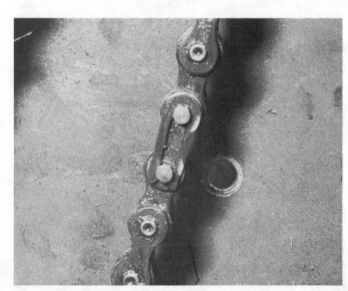

60

61

63

62

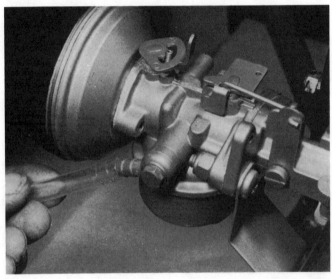

64

63 Connect the lower end of the vertical link to the same hole in the throttle lever (near the base of the engine) that it came out of during dismantling. Insert the threaded top of the link into the bellcrank and fit the serrated link adjuster screw arrowed in the photo. Fit the throttle cable bracket complete with the throttle cable.

64 Connect the fuel pipe onto the carburettor push-on fitting.

65 Connect the throttle cable to the throttle connector.

66 Fit the engine inner cowl.

67 Fit the engine outer cowl complete with recoil starter.

68 Fit the starter handle mounting onto the handle bar.

65

66

68

67a

67b

Recoil Starter Repair

1   Remove the engine outer cowl.
2   Remove the split pin from the starter shaft. Be prepared to take spring pressure as the pin is freed.
3   Lift off the washer, retainer plate, coil spring and pawls.
4   Lift the pulley off the shaft.
5   To fit a new cord, remove the handle from the old cord. Thread the new cord in between the pulley flanges, feed it through the hole in the pulley and tie a knot in the end (see Chapter 2 for details). Thread the other end of the cord through the handlebar mounting and fit the handle to the cord.

6   To fit a new recoil spring, hook the outer end of the spring onto the post in the housing. Wind the spring anti-clockwise from outside to inside of the spring dish. Place a little grease on the coils.
7   Fit the pulley onto the shaft and turn it anti-clockwise until it seats right in and engages with the hook at the inner end of the spring.

6

8   Place the coil spring on the shaft. If broken or damaged, renew it.

9   Check the condition of the pawls. Renew them if they are worn at the outer tip which engages with the starter hub. Fit the pawls onto the stub shafts.

10 Place the retainer plate on the shaft with the tab at each end pointing downwards. Engage each tab in the slot in the pawl (see photo 11).

11 Press the retaining plate down against the spring. Fit the washer. Insert the split pin and spread the legs of the pin.

10

8

11

9

12 Position the complete outer cowling near the engine so that the recoil starter is the same distance from the handle mounting as it will be when assembled on the engine. Tension the pulley by turning it anti-clockwise 3 turns. Wind the slack cord onto the pulley while holding pulley tension. Gently release the pulley.

13 Fit the outer cowling onto the engine as described previously. Pull the starter handle and check free movement and a positive return action of the handle.

Technical Data

Spark plug gap	0.025 in (0.635 mm)
Valve clearance:	
Inlet	0.006 in (0.15 mm)
Exhaust	0.010 in (0.25 mm)
Piston ring gap	N/A
Crankshaft endfloat	N/A

Oil: good quality 20/50 multi grade.
Petrol: recommended grade is 92 octane (2-star).

Index

Note: *The first number given is the page, the second (given in brackets) the paragraph number(s).*

Printed by
J H Haynes & Co Ltd
Sparkford Nr Yeovil
Somerset BA22 7JJ England